LIEUTENANT IN
ALGERIA

Jean-Jacques Servan-Schreiber

LIEUTENANT IN
ALGERIA

Translated from the French by Ronald Matthews

19 ✦ 57

New York: Alfred A. Knopf

Preface

There is only one war going on in the world today, the war that France is waging in Algeria.

Drafted, as I was, into the French army of Africa, I lived in the heart of this strange war, along with all the other young Frenchmen who were my comrades-in-arms. When I got back to France, I told our story, the story of what has been going on in Algeria these last three years and is still going on today. Other people have published their stories, too. These stories, which are all alike, are little by little helping to give our fellow countrymen the background they need if they are to appreciate the magnitude of the issues involved and find a solution which shall be at once human, worthy of France, and worthy of the Algerian people.

Now I have been asked if this book can be published abroad. I have agreed, despite the unvarnished picture it presents of certain aspects of French policy and certain weaknesses of the French army.

I have agreed because, in so far as what it portrays goes beyond the inadequacy of all men in all political struggles, I think it may persuade those people in the world who are still concerned with the history of France that my country retains a faith and an energy which will yet permit her to surmount her present sea of troubles.

When one has seen many men as magnificent as the ones I knew rising in revolt against the vicious circle of violence and the temptation to use brute force, one can be proud of one's country. I am. And these men's story should be known.

It will show those who are honestly looking for a way out of this war that the very nature of the struggle rules out any solution other than trusting France.

J.J.S.S.

P.S. *Certain of my comrades-in-arms have, like me, been demobilized, others are still in the army, still others are regulars. All of them have a right to expect that I shall take proper precautions to prevent their being identified. The changes necessary to ensure this have therefore been made in the story that follows.*

Contents

Part One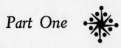

The War

Unfamiliar Terms *Appearing in the Text*

Chasseurs: a special infantry unit with armored vehicles.

Douar: an Algerian village consisting of several *mechtas*.

Goumiers: special native troops used in the French army.

Harka: a band of native soldiers; the word suggests that the men are rough and picturesque in appearance.

Jebel: a type of mountain, steep but not very high, which is characteristic of the Algerian countryside beyond the coastal plains.

Kachabia: the classic woolen headcloth worn by the Moslems of North Africa.

Mechta: an Arab house of molded earth, deep red in color, with a straw roof.

What is the best way of starting this story?

When I flip over the newspapers of all those months of summer, of autumn, of winter, it is the official face of the war in Algeria I see through their pages. The daily communiqués, all equally flat, spell out a litany of place names we all knew.

"At L'Arba, M. Boualem, a plumbing contractor, has been seriously wounded. . . ."

"Near Palestro, an infantry unit engaged a rebel band. . . ."

"At Ménerville, a Moslem has been found with his throat cut. . ."

"At Fondouk, a farm has been raided. . . ."

"At Rivet, in southern Algeria, a powerful bomb has exploded in the offices of a transport company. . . ."

"In the Sakamody area, the rebels have attacked. . . ."

Is there anyone who still reads these monotonous reports which have appeared day after day for months, almost for years?

Let us pick out at random one of these colorless items, as meaningless as the rest:

"Yesterday at Brahim, the occupants of a truck machine-gunned people in the street. Fortunately, only one man was wounded."

Nothing particularly out of the ordinary happened in the little village that day, nothing much more than is happening every day in village after village up and down this immense country. Just what did happen, though?

I will start from there.

Chapter One

1/ In the village of Brahim, as in any other village, there is a casbah. Algiers has its own, the best-known, which is just The Casbah. But every town, big or small, has its casbah too. People talk of "the L'Arba casbah" or "the Rivet casbah." It is simply the part of the town where the Moslems live.

On the aerial photographs that are used to prepare the type of operation known as "cleaning up a casbah," it stands out at once. It forms a thick, dark mass that looks as if it were the shadow thrown by the European town. The boundaries of a casbah, of course, are rarely clear-cut; the two communities live in a sort of mutual penetration. And the army is everywhere.

The Brahim casbah is on the way out of the village on the road to Keddara and Palestro. Along the road, which becomes a street, are a handful of shops and the Moorish café, where the Moslems talk the whole day through and which serves as the exchange of the "Arab telephone."

That particular Tuesday it was still very hot at five in the afternoon. Nerves were on edge, and not only because of the heat. There had been no let-up in the terrorism. Only yesterday the French postman, a man whom everyone liked, with twenty-five years in the village behind him, a conscientious worker and a good fellow, had been found at the start of his round with his throat cut. . . . People got used to it, of course, because the same sort of thing happened two or three times a week. But each time the tension was a little worse: people were just that much cagier about going out.

At one of the café's wooden tables two Arabs were just saying good-by. One was young, in flannel trousers and an open-neck shirt. The other, in a brown-and-white *kachabia*, had a gray beard and a face crisscrossed with wrinkles. The old man stayed in his seat, slowly finishing his glass of tea. The young man got up briskly and made for the street.

There was the bellow of an army motor horn and the nerve-racking shriek of brakes being jammed on hard. Everybody turned around.

A pale-yellow jeep had nearly run down the young Arab, who had not looked where he was going. He was not hurt, apart from the shock. But he started taking it out on the two French soldiers, whose jeep had stopped dead in the middle of the street, its engine stalled by the abrupt halt. He waved his arms and shouted at them—in Arabic, to be on the safe side.

Sergeant Baral started his engine again. He had no love for Arabs in general, and particularly for those who allowed themselves to shout at him, but this afternoon he had no time for emotional side-issues. With his escort, Private Geronimo, he was taking the mail to the regimental headquarters. He could settle accounts with this tiresome young hothead another day. There would be no difficulty in finding him: the village was not a big one.

"You dirty gook, stop your yowling or I'll give you a bellyful of lead," Geronimo shouted, to drown the voice of the Arab, who continued his wailing.

He jumped down from the jeep and described with his tommy-gun, which was hanging on a strap from his neck and resting on his stomach, the instinctive regulation quarter-turn to the right which puts it into the firing position.

The Arab stopped shouting. You could see his temper only in his black eyes and in the trembling of his long, dry hands.

The customers in the Moorish café sat motionless, looking out into the street. The proprietor, his hands full of glasses of tea, had stopped in his tracks with his back to the street, his head turned so as to follow the scene.

The Arab's silence relaxed the tension on the faces a little. But no one moved an inch: the jeep was still there, and so was Geronimo, with his tommy-gun trained. The Arab, standing squarely in front of him, seemed to be putting all his pride into his refusal to budge.

Geronimo had an almost irresistible desire to prolong the scene. He was the center of it. Everything depended on him. He liked that. It was an extraordinary feeling he had had since he had been in Algeria, one he had never experienced with his family or among his pals at Nice: this feeling of power, this domination of people, this tenfold increase in virility which his long, hard weapon gave him.

And here were all these spectators, spellbound by his movements and his looks, their eyes fixed on the barrel of his tommy-gun—awaiting his pleasure. If he wanted to spin the enjoyment out, he had only to forbid the whole lot to move, starting with that old bastard who was coming over to calm down his pal.

"Gero, don't be a son of a bitch. We've no time to waste. You can have your fun another time. Come on, jump in!"

Baral had had enough: he did not like to see his friend getting into that sort of state. And then he was in command of the vehicle, and responsible for the mail arriving on time. He could see from the sudden curl that had appeared at the corner of Geronimo's mouth that if the fun went on any longer, there would be no holding him. As with a thoroughbred, there was a certain threshold he must not be allowed to reach, for beyond it he would become deaf, completely physical and unpredictable.

The old man shuffled forward cautiously with heavy feet, as if approaching an animal that must not be frightened. Before he set foot in the roadway, he addressed his Arab friend from the edge of the pavement in a soothing voice: "Go home. Come on, don't be mulish. Come on, go home. . . ." He spoke in French so that there should be no misunderstanding with the soldiers.

A harsh detonation tore the air and cut into the quick of all the tense nerves. The old man leaned forward, holding his stomach with his hands, and collapsed softly, muttering to himself unintelligibly, while his blood flowed down from the sidewalk to the cobbles of the street. His eyes, which were still open and conscious, remained fixed on the jeep, as if he were anxious at what more might follow.

Geronimo, who had not stirred an inch, stared at his tommy-gun with the calm of a man who has come down to earth again. It had "gone off" by itself, independent of his will, as if it had been a living organ in which all the tension outside and all the tension within him had accumulated until they had reached flash point and had to discharge themselves.

Now that the orgasm was over and a wounded man was in his death throes at his feet, Geronimo was trembling a little. Motionless, he awaited his companion's orders.

2/ Geronimo was a more attractive young man than most of the other troops. To begin with, his appearance was striking. He was very handsome, and his good looks had become a legend in the regiment. Our colonel, who had taken a liking to him, had nicknamed him the "Black Angel." He liked what is euphemistically called "rough-housing," and when he did not get it—this war is so monotonous—he provoked it. He was not the only one, though: everyone likes that. And, anyway, he had a lot of guts: when a real rough-house did turn up, when we had armed men up against us, some of our comrades would turn cautious and sing a different tune, but Geronimo was happier than ever. Shooting was what he liked.

I met him first in rather special circumstances.

We had been in Algeria over a month and we had already taken part in a number of local operations, but Geronimo was not in my company, and training was carried out on the company level. At dinnertime one night in the officers' mess I saw Lieutenant Martin arriving, a little late, in a magnificent camouflaged parachutist's outfit which had lost its color and been stretched to his enormous size by several years in Indochina.

Martin was beaming. Addressing me, he said: "We're going out on night patrol. Be ready at curfew time, nine o'clock. Luminous watch, and nothing in your pockets: mustn't make a noise marching. No tin hats, and—you're dark, that's O.K., nothing on the head—a black scarf for the fair-haired boys. Eat enough so you won't be hungry till tomorrow. And don't put on a pullover or a shirt. It's cold at night, but you're going to be warm."

Martin was operations officer. He was a regular officer promoted from the ranks, with twelve years of service and fifteen mentions in dispatches; he knew army regulations by heart, but treated them with common sense, and he loved command. The men trusted him because it was obvious that he knew what he was doing: war was his job. He wasn't too fond of the reservists: he found they were soft, apathetic, and knew nothing of an infantryman's job. But he took them as they came, and endeavored, by his prestige and his talent for command, to get the best out of this mediocre instrument.

"Well, how's things?"

He looked at me with shining eyes and a self-satisfied, provocative smile that was belied by his friendly tone. With people who did not share his opinions, he tried even harder than with others to "take them in hand," to drag them with kindly firmness out of their dreams to face his universal reality, the war to the death against the Communist conspiracy.

I smiled back. I liked him a lot. He never lied and didn't intrigue, which is exceptional and makes life easier.

He went on to explain what was up.

"There are some Viets in the spot we're going to. I don't know how many, it's the third time they've done a job there. Last week they sawed through all the telegraph poles, thirty in a single night, so there must be ten of them, at least. The Second Company repaired the poles. They did it again two days later. Then, the day before yesterday at nightfall, the son of the Sintès, who've got a farm there, was killed in a field. We'll never find them in daytime. If we go there by night, there's just a chance. In any case, it'll give them a fright and us some exercise. There are no two ways with the Viets: you've got to move faster than they do. That makes them keep quiet."

In Martin's mouth, the Algerian *fellagha* were always the Viets. For him and for many of his fellow regulars who had served in Indochina it was the shortest and the clearest way of preventing any ambiguity: there was the army on one side and the Communists on the other. It was essential that the reservists—"who've read a lot of nonsense in the papers" —should get that well into their heads.

At nine o'clock, in the little yard of the farm where operational headquarters had been set up, the men of the patrol, picked by Martin, were gathered around the jeeps that were waiting for them, headlights out and windshields down. There was an unaccustomed silence. Although the operation was to take place eighteen miles away, there was not one of us, as we emerged into the open—crossing that extraordinary wall of the curfew, beyond which, every night, all life stops in the Algerian countryside—who was not nervous about giving the alarm by a word or a sound.

To the left of our darkened route there rose, somber and mysterious, those southern mountains which we had never yet approached, and whose acquaintance we were about to make that silent summer night. Far away to the right, a halo of white-and-orange iridescence in the sky reflected the myriad lights of a big town. That was Algiers, so near and yet so far—Algiers, which we had never seen since the day we had landed there and been handed literature, postcards, and little bags of comforts by young and pretty girl students, voluntary workers in the French Algeria movement.

In the half-light of a moon screened by a stormcloud, a milestone informed us: PALESTRO, 25 KILOMETERS. We were there.

Martin fixed the details of the operation, and then found a spot where the men going out on the patrol could take a rest till the moon had gone down. He beckoned to another officer and me to follow him.

"While we're waiting, I'm taking you over the way to see the Sintès, whose son was killed. . . . They'll tell us the story." He added, with his provocative smile: "You're going to see some settlers, real ones—not the sort they invent in Paris."

The shutters were closed at the Sintès' and the lights were out. Martin asked as we went in that everyone speak in a whisper and that there should be no light but our flashlights. The aim was to give no indication of anything unusual to the lookouts who were almost certainly posted, as they were every evening, on the hill overlooking the farm.

The farmer, Sintès, was alone in the room. He was in his forties, a sturdy figure, but his drawn features and his slow movements spoke of an immense lassitude. He received us courteously, as if he were cheered by the presence of visitors after those two interminable nights of solitary sorrow, and he gave us the details that Martin had come to get.

His son had been coming back from work that night with a friend. Coming toward them on the path, from the opposite direction, they saw a group of three young Arabs who had been friends of theirs since their days at the village school.

Young Sintès and his friend had not seen them for over two months and had thought they had taken to the *maquis*. That had been a rather surprising report, for the Sintès had known these Arabs as quiet types with no particular politics; after they had got used to the idea the Sintès had begun to feel a new respect for them: they had chosen danger and the hard life. No doubt they were enemies, but you can respect men who join up for a tough fight, whatever it is.

So when young Sintès and his friend saw the three coming along the path that night after their long absence, they told themselves that the taking to the *maquis* had been just a romantic figment of their imagination. After all, here they were, returning along the same road, carefree and happy to be back again.

As the two groups approached each other, they raised their voices to exchange greetings.

"Hi, Pierre, how goes it?" shouted one of the Arabs.

"Hullo, my lad. Where have you been all this time?" replied Sintès. Turning to his friend, he said in a lower voice: "Extraordinary the ideas you can get into your head. Since this business started, you find yourself seeing bogy men everywhere. I could have sworn these guys were in *fellagha* uniform already and commanding patrols in the Aurès. What silly nonsense! It's good to see them around again."

"That's when they killed him. They pulled their guns out of their jackets and fired point-blank," old Sintès said. He concluded: "My son's friend, Jean Soler, took to his heels and escaped by the skin of his teeth. He's wounded in the arm. He's in the hospital in Algiers, almost off his head. He told us the whole story, but it was a job getting him to talk. He hasn't stopped crying for three days, and now and then he shouts. He'd never believed that things like that could happen. . . .

"Would you like another drink, gentlemen?" said Sintès.

His wife was in the room. We noticed her all of a sudden; we had not seen her enter. She was a shadow; she barely existed, her eyes were almost shut. Doubtless she had joined us out of politeness, but she did not say a word or make a movement, and her presence in the room, with its eerie light shed by the flashlights we were pointing at the floor, imposed silence on us. We stayed like that for a minute or two, awed by her presence, and each of us for a moment turned his eyes within.

Martin got up and put his glass on the table. Still without a word, he walked toward the door. We followed him.

Before he crossed the threshold, he turned round. Mme Sintès held out her hand to him.

"*Au revoir, Madame,*" Martin said gravely. "We're going to do all we can tonight to avenge your son. Don't worry. . . . And the French army is going to stay on now to protect Algeria. He won't have died for nothing."

"What a damned fool! He could have shut his trap instead of making propaganda. Makes me sick!" the second lieutenant whispered as we went out.

It was not propaganda. Martin believed it.

It was midnight, and Martin had gathered the ten men of the patrol around him.

"Synchronize your watches. It's 0003 hours. We're all leaving together, in single file, six feet between each two men. Not a word once we're out of the door. We're going to march due south for about an hour, along the side of the mountain, in the gorge you see there. When I give the signal, we'll split up. You"—and he pointed to me—"take four men with you and cross over to the other side of the *wadi*. I'll go on with the others along this slope. Radio contact at the hour and the half-hour. My call sign is Lima, you're Lima 1, and the fixed radio of the post here will be Lima 2. As long as there's no trouble, you'll transmit a short whistle when I call you at contact time. Nothing more. If the moon gets up again, don't march in the open: stay in the shadows as much as you can. Look out for dogs—they're the ones that'll pick you up. Never fire first: if you think you see a shadow, it's an even chance that it's another man of the patrol. Wait till you're certain. The moment you hear firing, come to the help of the patrol that's engaged, without getting into its field of fire. Recognition signal: dash-dot-dash. Acknowledgment: dot-dash-dot. Password: Masséna. Countersign: Metz. Any questions?"

There could have been a dozen questions, or none at all. Anyway, Martin did not wait.

While the others were making a final check of their pockets and working the bolts of their tommy-guns or their rifles, Martin took me by the arm and led me aside.

"I just wanted to tell you: there are two men here who've been sent by Biaggi.[1] I'm not too fond of guys who play politics in the army, even if I'm inclined to share their opinions, but it wasn't I who brought them here. You'll find a bit of everything in this rag-bag of reservists. These two have got one strong point: they're not just full of hot air. What I wanted to say was, I'm putting one in your patrol. I can guess what you're going to think, but I know what I'm doing. It's better this way. You'll have to have them one day

---

[1] Maître Biaggi, an extreme-right-wing lawyer and a former hero of De Lattre's army who formed the militia body called the "Volunteers of the French Union."

or another. This evening's a good time to begin. The night and the danger'll put things in proper perspective."

Martin got a man and brought him over to my patrol, which was ready to start. He was well built, festooned with grenades, and had a sack hanging down in front of him with six tommy-gun magazines in it. A dagger was at his left side. Close to, he had a good-looking face, full of excitement. Martin told me his name, and I shook his hand. It was Geronimo.

3/ In the Brahim casbah the man Geronimo had murdered was still losing blood and looking out into the street. Lying on his side along the edge of the sidewalk, he clasped his stomach with his hands and did not say a word.

Sergeant Baral had got out of the jeep, with the despairing but resigned air of a man who once more had to put up with a friend's follies. He did not like this sort of thing anyway. He hated the gooks, but killing was a dirty business. He got no physical kick out of it. Still, from time to time, it was a nasty job you had to go through. Geronimo was his pal, and he was not going to leave him in the lurch.

The sound of voices and of running feet could be heard from the center of the village. Obviously the noise of the shot and the immediate flight of all the Arabs from the Moorish café had been heard there.

"Come on, jump in. We're getting the hell out of here."

Baral pushed an openmouthed and unresisting Geronimo into the jeep and drove off.

All that was left in the street was the murdered man. Another little trickle of blood was beginning to run along his mouth. His face, astonishingly calm for a man who has been shot in the stomach, was lit up directly now by the sun, which was setting at the far end of the road. The deserted casbah might have been a mausoleum.

The sounds came nearer. Around the corner of the street appeared a group of men in civilian clothes, each of them carrying a gun. Quickly they surrounded the wounded man. Everyone was talking at once.

"Don't stop here, you ninnies, or you'll get yourselves picked off like rabbits. There's nothing worse than the casbah for enfilading fire. You, take charge of this street. You, post yourself at that corner there. You two, stop every vehicle coming into the village."

Prato shouted louder than the others. In theory, he was the commander of the village territorials, and when he was on duty he was addressed as Captain Prato. He was a reserve captain, with three mentions in dispatches for the French campaign. He had about thirty men under his orders: almost all the Brahim men between twenty and forty-five who were capable of carrying and using a firearm.

They formed the "territorial unit" (U.T.) that is to be found in every town or village in Algeria. The U.T. everywhere is equipped with two sets of arms. A stock of modern weapons (machine guns, American automatic rifles, tommyguns) is deposited in one house in the village and reserved for grave emergencies. Then there are lighter individual weapons (rifles, shotguns, revolvers), and each territorial keeps one of these in his home. In theory, the men are at the disposal of the local military command. In practice, there are often reasons—a job or family responsibilities—which prevent them from answering the summons of the sector commander. But they are not idle: they take turns doing sentry duty round the village at night; they mount their own "operations," searches and supervision of the Arab inhabitants; and occasionally when there is a more serious "job" afoot they may go to replace their territorial colleagues of another village, who sometimes prefer not to be recognized after jobs of this type.

The time a man spends on territorial service is not given free. It is well paid by the Government-General. Each territorial draws the equivalent of military pay. What is more, it is a pleasant excuse for the men to get together one or two evenings a week.

The difficulty of using territorials for regular operations is their little habit of using arms for private ends, which, when discovered, has often provoked minor marital scandals. As a result, the military authorities have more and more frequently called for the dissolution of the U.T. in the villages.

A classic scenario then develops. The territorials unleash their mayor, who alarms all his contacts in Algiers. His contacts then knock on every door in the Government-General and demand the transfer of the officer—most likely a fellow traveler—who has dared to suggest the dissolution. The civil authorities get out of these delicate affairs by rendering a Pontius Pilate kind of justice. The territorials are not dissolved, the officer is not transferred, and the mayor invites civilians and soldiers to lunch together to dissipate the misunderstandings and to reunite both sides for the good of their common ideal.

The Brahim territorial unit had now assembled at almost full strength, with its arms at the ready, everyone talking and gesticulating around the wounded Arab or at the entrance to the deserted streets of the casbah.

"The swine, they've made a nasty mess of him. You see who it is?"

"No, don't know him."

"It's Larbi, the ex-serviceman who lives there"—pointing to a mud-walled shack at the far end of the village. "He came to the get-together they organized on Saturday. There weren't many of them; only three, I fancy, out of twenty.

The rest had the wind up about being seen with Frenchmen. I said to myself: these three have cooked their goose, all right. The bastards will get them, like the others. . . . That's it, it's starting all over again."

"Right in the middle of the village. They've got nerve, all right! And it'll be just like yesterday, nobody will have seen anything, that's for sure."

"Anyway, there's no one *to* see. They've all hit the road. That shows they've got a guilty conscience."

One of the territorials had bent over the wounded man, who was now in his death throes, his eyes popping out of their sockets.

"What are you talking about? It's not Larbi at all."

"What, it's not Larbi?"

"No, it can't be. Larbi didn't have this scar on the cheek."

"Yes, he did. But, look, it doesn't matter whether it's Larbi or someone else; it's all the same. If they've bumped him off, it's because he was on our side."

"You're right there. But I don't think it is Larbi."

A truck that had just crossed the village drew up level with the two territorials who had been posted in the roadway twenty yards from the Moorish café.

"Stop it!" Prato shouted.

The truck had already stopped, right in front of the crowd in the middle of the street. It was one of the Arbatache mine trucks. They came every morning to pick up the Moslem workers who lived in Brahim and brought them back every evening about seven.

In the driver's cabin of the dumptruck there were two Arabs, and three others were in the back. They were all on the young side, with open-necked shirts, jeans, and the invariable knitted caps on their heads.

They were among the lucky ones. Most of their comrades were out of work, or at least had no regular work.

Of course, there was the wine harvest, for which labor was taken on every year, but that did not last long. From time to time the army ordered a construction job. But of the three businesses that had given full-time jobs to the Brahim Moslem workers, one—the road-building works—had been forced to shut down and another to give up employing native labor. The *fellagha* had got what they wanted. By picking on fairly well-known workers in each business, letting everyone know that if they went on working for the French they would be punished, and then carefully slitting the throats of those they had picked, they had emptied the workshop. A little later one of the Arab workers who had stayed on at the cement works had, in his turn, set fire to a shed. The management could not continue to take such risks, for the insurance companies refused coverage.

The result was that since midsummer only the Arbatache mine, a branch of a big Franco-Italian company, had continued to employ labor. The company had asked for and got permanent protection by the army. A half-section—fifteen men—was assigned to guard the mine on the spot, and a military post with two heavy machine guns and a mortar had been built on the ground overlooking it, to command the approaches. To protect labor on this scale in the whole of Algeria would have required an army of two million men, so it was protected where it could be.

"Bring them here!"

The reserve sergeant who was Prato's second-in-command in the territorials told the driver to drive past the Moorish café and park his truck on the right.

The sun was almost down by now and was lighting the street less brightly: a breath of air, the first cool air of the day, was caressing the faces of the group. The face of the wounded man was now contorted with pain. When they passed in front of him, the workers in the truck, already visibly disturbed by this congregation of armed territorials, began to tremble in every limb and huddled against one another. They feared the worst.

The worst had happened at Ameur the week before: a lynching. When such an access of fever and of physical frenzy seizes the European population of this or that village, exasperated by a series of *fellagha* murders, the police and the army are helpless: the only way they can hold back the wave is by firing on their compatriots. So they let the wave pass, hoping that the Arabs are not fools enough to stay out of doors. The gook-hunt starts. In a small town, by the time the fun is over, there will be two or three of them lying in the street: more, of course, in a big one. One cannot do anything about it. It is a phenomenon like avalanches in snowy countries. You have to live with the thing. You get used to it.

You also get used to the communiqués that the Government-General conscientiously issues on such occasions for the benefit of the public. On the evening of the L'Arba affair, there was this conclusion, in the always astonishing official style:

"*The authorities cannot too strongly warn the public against individual reactions.*"

In the obvious excitement of the men who were fussing about round the bleeding body at the entrance to the alleys of the casbah, the Arbatache workers thought they could detect the symptoms of this fever, which was their nightmare. An accident had occurred, and the exasperated territorials were going to take vengeance. The Arabs felt that at any price they must avoid staying there or they would end up as the quarry of the day.

Prato did not speak Arab, and he knew that when Moslems are scared they become completely incapable of using what French they know. The only way to surmount their panic is by means of pain—after several fast blows they may remember a little French. But Prato had no time to lose. He called for a colleague who spoke Arab and began to question the driver.

The driver trembled like a leaf. The more he stammered, the angrier Prato and the others grew, and the more they shouted at him, the worse he shook. The dialogue became completely nonsensical. They would have to beat him up.

The noise of another vehicle, arriving at high speed, distracted their attention. It was an army Dodge containing a few soldiers.

Just as it drew to a halt, a volley of shots filled the air. The Arab truck had taken advantage of the distraction and started to make a getaway. Six hunting guns fired after it, but it was already out of range, racing toward Keddara.

"What's up?" the sergeant sitting beside the driver in the army vehicle shouted to the territorials.

The shouting of the territorials, who continued to fire wildly after the fleeing truck, and the body he saw lying on the pavement conveyed absolutely nothing to Sergeant Mauré. Very excited, he got out of his truck and bore down on Prato's second-in-command, who was the nearest to him.

"Come on, now, what's all this about?"

"You can see for yourself. The swine have bumped some guy off again. We heard the shots, and we got here in no time. We tried to stop a truck with six gooks in it, but they beat it before we had time to identify them: they're obviously the ones who did the job. . . ."

"What's the army waiting for?" shouted another. "You got any objection to running the bastards down? You're going to let them get away with it, as usual. . . ."

The recent series of crimes had set the nerves of the whole population on edge, and the territorials' sense of impotence exasperated them.

"Perhaps you want an affidavit before you go after the *fellagha?* You'd like us to give you the number of their truck, wouldn't you?" And, turning to a friend: "I'm damned if I know what need we have of these bums. We'd be better off if we took care of the gooks ourselves and counted the army out—then we'd settle the job. We're too soft, that's the trouble."

Mauré's head was on fire. He was an accountant in the Limoges office of the French Railways, married for just a year, a pleasant and friendly sort. Since he had been called up as a reserve sergeant in July, the only jobs he had been given had been routine escort duties with nothing to worry about. Everyone else had some "scrap" to tell of. But he—it just happened that way—had never been in a tough spot. His holiday in Algeria had been peaceful and monotonous, and he asked only one thing: that it should remain so. Now here he was, without a moment to think things out, catapulted into a situation where he had to act immediately. One corpse, twenty extremely excited territorials, a band of *fellagha* fleeing in a truck, the army to the rescue—and the army was himself.

Mauré was a quiet type, but he was not a coward. If there was a chance of doing in some real stinkers, caught in the act—usually it was only "suspects," people the authorities didn't have the goods on—he would have to give them the works, whatever the cost. After all, why else was he here?

"We'll get moving," said Mauré. "We'll run them down and we'll give them the works as soon as we catch them. No time to get reinforcements. But call the CO at once at HQ and tip him off; ask him to send up the armor to cut the road to Palestro: that'll corner them. So long now . . ."

"So long, and try not to miss them. We're getting fed up."

The Arab truck had disappeared over the horizon. Mauré told the driver to step on the gas. The Dodge was much more powerful and should be able to overtake the truck, but night was falling and they had to move quickly. In the back, the eight soldiers were automatically loading their weapons and dividing the lookout on the road, four to the right and four to the left.

4/ The regimental HQ had been set up on the side of the mountain, in an old stone building that had been built by nuns for a girls' school.

When we arrived in the area, the nuns were finishing their packing. The officer who had contacted them on behalf of the military authorities of the sector had asked them not to leave, not to give up their work and their pupils. But they had no more pupils. Why? The young Moslem girls were afraid to come. "But we'll go and get them, we'll bring them here under military escort and protect them. . . . Sister, you've no right to desert," the officer had said feelingly. "Your duty is to stay on here at any cost."

The Superior, an old lady in midnight-blue robes and white coif, had put on her sweetest expression, as if to soften her reply. "At any cost? No, major. If your turn has come, it's not ours any longer. We can't live together. We shall always be on the side of our pupils. Don't hold it against me. You're doing your job, as you see your duty. We're doing ours. No doubt we shall come back one day—when you're gone."

Major Henry, second-in-command of the regiment, was a well-brought-up man, and he had made no response. He was in a furious temper, and he came out, exploding: "It's just like it was in Indochina, the priests and the nuns let us

down everywhere. They're always on the side of our enemies. It's not even as if they got anything out of it: once
we're kicked out, they haven't got long to stay. You'd think
they would understand that, but no—it's all starting again
here. It's pure insanity. You see, my dear fellow, that's why
it's so hopeless. The struggle between Christian civilization
and Communism just isn't fair: we'll lose every time. You
don't win wars by turning the other cheek. Everything's
mucked up."

In the disused presbytery Henry, tall and lean with curly
fair hair, was planning an operation for the next day with
some staff officers. The enemy he was up against was represented in our sector by a man with a clear-cut name: Kodja.

Kodja had a big reputation as a fighter. Within a single
year he had recruited and organized the best rebel network
in southeast Algeria. He commanded a number of bands,
with about thirty men in each. The one which was operating
in our sector had lost about half its strength in a recent engagement. We knew that if we gave it a bare three weeks' respite, it would be able to re-form completely, thanks to recruits from the young Moslems who were eager to join the
maquis. So we had to wipe it out in the brief period while it
was still weak—otherwise, the whole job would have to be
started over again.

That was the aim of the operation Major Henry was preparing. But he was launching it, to some extent, in the dark,
for he had no sure information as to where the rebel band
was holed up at the moment. It had shown no sign of life
since the last engagement, preoccupied as it was with building up its strength.

The field telephone on the kitchen table, which Henry
used for working, rang. It was Prato, of the Brahim territorials. He reported to the major what had just happened.

His report, stuffed with minute details about the spirit and initiative shown by the men of the U.T., went on endlessly. Henry was annoyed; but the information filtering through this flood of words seemed serious enough for him to contain his impatience and listen to the end.

In brief, a motorized *fellagha* commando had raided the village. Fortunately, there had only been one casualty, an Arab, for the territorials had been on the spot at once, as soon as the first shot was fired, and had put the *fellagha* truck to flight. On Prato's information, an army Dodge belonging to the regiment had given chase to the rebels immediately. The sergeant of the Dodge asked to be reinforced by machine-gun carriers so as to cut off the murderers' escape.

Henry thanked Prato. Before hanging up, he told him to get his men back home and not to let them embroider their doings that evening in the village cafés, with the usual effect of alarming their fellow citizens by lurid details of the *fellagha* crimes. The details might only too often, alas, be accurate—as in the horrible story of Sintès's son—but they had the worst possible effect on the calmness of the population, which was just what the Viets wanted.

Henry considered. The affair could not be sneezed at. A motorized commando? That could only be Kodja's men. He summoned two second lieutenants of his staff and gave them the usual instructions:

"Contact the armored detachment of Marshal Joffre at once and tell them to send two machine-gun carriers to support one of our cars which has given chase to a truckload of rebels.

"Alert the two companies whose quarters are on the Keddara road and order them to stand by, armed and ready by their vehicles; their orders are to take action at the first exchange of fire.

"Make contact with Air Support in Algiers."

Henry added, as if talking to himself: "Pity it was Mauré, he's not so quick on the job. I'm afraid he'll let them get away."

The telephone rang again. It was the duty officer. He reported to Henry that two of his men, Sergeant Baral and Private Geronimo, asked if he could see them at once.

What could that mean? Henry did not like complications, and he knew there were a lot too many with those two. But he liked Geronimo: he was always volunteering for tough jobs.

"Tell them to come in."

Baral told the story of the afternoon's incident with an air of indifference. He agreed that Geronimo had behaved a little excitedly, but he added that if his tommy-gun had gone off, he really wasn't to be blamed. This particular weapon had come in a consignment from the Saint Eugène factory which suffered—this was quite true—from a nasty defect. In a certain position, the round in the barrel could go off without the trigger being squeezed; the mere pressure of the palm of the hand on the safety catch was sufficient. Baral himself had reported the defect and had demonstrated when the commander-in-chief had come over from Algiers on an inspection the week before. The general had told one of the colonels in his party to make a note that the entire stock of Saint Eugènes in the regiment should be replaced without delay. Nothing had been done, however. So Geronimo's responsibility was objectively very much smaller. It might very well be true that he had not squeezed the trigger.

That was not the problem now, though. Henry had already linked the story up with the other affair and smelled a rat: wasn't the man Geronimo had wounded the same as the victim of the terrorist commando Prato had reported? But if that was so, who the devil were Mauré and his men chasing?

That question would answer itself eventually. Anyway, there was nothing much to worry about: if the Arabs in the truck were running away, they'd obviously been up to some dirty work. It would do no harm to run them down.

The telephone rang again. The radio-operator had received an urgent message to be passed to the colonel or his second-in-command, Henry.

The message came from one of the mountain posts, the one called Valmy. The points where our troops had been posted in the mountains had, as often as not, no names on the maps, so they had been christened out of French history.

"Valmy post reports that on the Marshal Joffre-Keddara-Palestro road, twelve miles from the village of Brahim, a Dodge truck apparently belonging to one of our units and identified from the post through field glasses has just opened fire on a vehicle occupied by Arabs which is still a hundred yards ahead of it. Valmy will report any developments. Over."

Well, we shall see, Henry told himself. Anyway, nobody could change anything now. Whether the gooks had played the fool, or whether it had been the territorials—the army, as usual, had no means of knowing and had to charge ahead in the mist, shouldering the burden for everyone.

"If only Mauré can fight," murmured Henry, whose opinion of the reservists was not high, though he had a certain liking for them.

5/ Mauré had planned his action skillfully. He was determined not to bungle it.

Because he often talked to Arabs in the street and was not interested in getting drunk or in certain other kinds of fun, and because he had not yet been involved in a scrap, the men in his company were beginning to look on him as a sissy. That had not worried him much until now, for his conscience was clear: if he had had no chance of getting into a rough-house, it was not his fault. He didn't go out looking for trouble, but he did not run away from it either.

Today everything was going to change, one way or the other. He had got his rough-house, and everyone in the regiment would know it by now. One of two things could happen. He might come back with his tail between his legs, and at one fell swoop all the barbed hints of the past would turn into unconcealed contempt. That didn't bear thinking of. Or he could direct his men with sufficient force to teach the *fellagha* a good lesson, and then he would step straight into the class of people who had the right, of an evening in the barrack room, to talk without being interrupted.

Mauré, with all his intelligence and his nerves concentrating on an objective he wanted passionately, was tense with the incredible hope of being, in everyone's eyes, from tomorrow on, a "man." He would be like the others, men who had been under fire and come out victorious—he, Reserve Sergeant Mauré, the tranquil Limoges bureaucrat, turned into a fierce and skillful commander.

The affair did not last long. Mauré, seeing that night was coming on, told his driver that when he had got within a certain distance of the rebel truck he was not to draw any closer. He ordered his men to fire from that range, but in the air; if the Arabs were innocent they might take this as a summons to stop, and if they were *fellagha* it might persuade them that his engine was giving out and that they had nothing to fear from his firing. Thus, he reckoned, the *maquisards*, who are always sparing with their ammunition, would hold their fire in the hope that nightfall would give them a chance to make good their getaway. Mauré also figured that his strategy would save his men unnecessary danger—the *fellagha* were good shots. Then, just as darkness fell, Mauré

planned to run the enemy down at top speed, with headlights on, and to open fire with all his guns at point-blank
range as he came alongside.

As the Arab truck continued its headlong flight, the operation was carried out without a hitch. At five minutes past
eight the Arbatache mine truck was in the ditch by the road
and the workers were riddled with bullets, killed on the spot.

Mauré thanked God that everything had gone so well,
and that his men—reservists like himself—had been able to
do their duty as soldiers without a single one being killed or
wounded. His nightmare was that he might one day have a
dead man or a disabled man on his conscience. Good old
Mauré.

6/ After two months of burning summer during which
you could never breathe, even at night, the wonders of the
Algerian autumn were upon us. What a grand country!
thought Major Henry.

Deliberately, savoring the silence of the countryside,
looking toward the horizon where Algiers with its lights had
taken up its nightly sentry duty, he turned his steps toward
the corrugated-iron garage where the officers' mess was in-
stalled.

Henry was a man of feeling. He liked to daydream, to
tell long stories that he romanticized with ease—it was his
way of detaching himself from the worries and responsibilities of his daily work. Dinner in the mess on an evening
when there was no operation ahead was a pleasure for him.
He could relax and amuse the others.

That evening he felt in good form. To start with, the
colonel would not be there: he had been summoned to Paris
by the Minister and would not be back until the day after
tomorrow. The raincoats Henry had been vainly sweating

himself blind for a month to get, applying to every quarter-master's store there was, had finally turned up; he would no longer have to put up with the sight of those idiot reservists mounting guard in shirt-sleeves in the pouring rain. Finally, the day had gone well: he had stood in for the colonel without difficulty, which was a satisfaction.

"Atten-shun!" thundered the voice of a second lieutenant, who always enjoyed making the other officers jump when the colonel or his second-in-command arrived in the mess.

The officers, standing at attention with smiles on their lips—Henry was a charmer—waited for the "At ease, gentlemen" that relaxes bodies and minds.

The conversation started up everywhere at once, as usual. With eight officers at the table, at least five subjects were being discussed simultaneously, and in every direction, without anyone being particularly interested or even hearing clearly what was said. But everyone could say his piece that way. This friendly and confusing hum went on until someone or other, whether it was by a sentence that was a little easier to hear or a remark that was a little more interesting, produced a spontaneous crystallization of the conversation.

Ten minutes went by before the huge Captain Martin, who was always jovial, did the trick.

"Well," he said, "it seems that Mauré has covered himself with glory."

He could count on his effect: glory interests everyone.

"Yes—still, let's not make too much of it," said Henry, in the sudden concentrated silence of the table. "He displayed a most commendable sense of initiative in the way he went after the runaways, and his speedy action must have had a good effect on the population of Brahim. Apart from that, there was no heavy fighting, and anyway Mauré didn't find a single weapon on the corpses."

"How come?"

"I don't know. Perhaps they tossed them out before the scuffle, in the night, so they could pick them up later if they got away with it. Perhaps one of them took off with the arms without Mauré's men seeing him. Perhaps they didn't have their arms with them. In any case, it's kind of a slippery business that the territorials have stuck their nose into, and I can't manage to sort it out. Mauré has done his duty satisfactorily, and that's that, but there's no need to give him a medal for it."

Henry did not want this subject to drag on: he did not like people talking shop at table.

"But what are we going to put in the evening report if there weren't any arms?"

Second Lieutenant Labrunie, a schoolmaster from the greater Paris area, had, as an intellectual, been assigned to draw up the information reports that were transmitted evening and morning to headquarters in Algiers. He had the physique of his character: square, short, stocky, with a flat nose and cropped fair hair—the living image of efficiency. He was a conscientious fellow and thought hard before every report. His share of the war in Algeria was to do this job well, so he pressed the point.

"So that's the way it is, Labrunie. If you want your work done for you, say so. That's it, you draw the pay, and then we do the job for you. Is there anything else you want tonight?"

Martin loved teasing these little reservists who even after two months of army life sometimes still bridled in front of their problems with the air of a young virgin before her first experience.

Labrunie did not like being taken for a virgin, nor for a sissy—that is to say a Parisian idealist (he was one of the few men in the regiment who did not come from the southwest of France).

"I don't care a damn, personally," he said. "I'll put down that they had arms, as usual. Only I warn you that if they ask for them in Algiers at the end of the month, you'll be hard put to produce them."

This question of arms involved us in a veritable acrobatics of accountancy. The regulations laid down that together with the dead counted after each "engagement" the nature of the arms recovered should be specified. That presented no difficulty as long as it was merely a question of entries in a book. But after a few administrative inquiries, up and down the army of Algeria, had shown that these entries were often pure imagination and the arms fictitious, the authorities had decreed that, in theory at least, the arms mentioned in the reports should be held for a possible check-up. Which necessitated greater accuracy or, when there were no arms, some juggling tricks. When there was a big haul of arms, you declared only part of them, so as to be able to keep some in reserve when there were not enough—or none at all. Unfortunately, when the reserve was exhausted—as was the case now —you could not put any arms in the report if there weren't any. That is why Labrunie had allowed himself to draw attention to this detail.

"All right, then, I'll say that no arms were captured."

"No, no. Don't be a damn fool. If you say that, there'll be an inquiry, and that'll screw us up with more paper work. We've got better things to do. If you haven't got any arms to put down, then don't put anything. Just mention the wounded man in the street, machine-gunned by the truck." [2]

There was nothing to worry about. If the civil authorities—in an attempt to cover up their own tomfooleries by

---

[2] The official report, communicated to the press, as every day, by the press office of the Government-General, with those of all the other areas of Algeria, simply said: "Yesterday at —— the occupants of a truck machine-gunned people in the streets. Fortunately, only one man was wounded."

making trouble for the army—by any chance kicked up a
rumpus about the other corpses of the day, one of two things
would happen.

The Government-General might request the Army
Command to carry out an inquiry. In that case, the request
would be passed on to the unit itself, and it would draw up
the report. There was nothing to worry about.

Otherwise, the inquiry would be demanded from the
administrative side, and it would be passed on to the village
gendarmes, who were all more or less relatives or friends of
the territorials and who would have nothing to gain by putting them in the soup. There was nothing to worry about
there either.

So Mauré would not get into any trouble.

The whole humdrum affair was simple and clear to the
realistic mind of a Martin. It was certainly of very small importance in Henry's eyes, by comparison with the dozens of
difficult concrete questions posed every day by the running
of a regiment on field service. As far as the teacher was concerned, it was a mere question of an entry in a book. But it
did not seem quite so unimportant to another regular captain who had just been assigned to us for a spell before taking command of a battalion.

He was a cautious fellow who almost never talked about
serious things. Nobody knew his opinions—which was why
people rather mistrusted him, for he was skillful at concealing
them behind a disarmingly amusing façade. This time he did
not seem so comfortable as usual. When he spoke up, it
was in a rather solemn voice that surprised and silenced
everyone else.

"Excuse me for butting in. I only wanted to suggest that
if Arabs are killed by our men and no arms are found on
them, you can't rule out the possibility that the victims
aren't *fellagha* but maybe honest guys from the village—

which wouldn't do much good to our relations with the population."

This cautious language did not quite make his point. "What are you trying to say?" asked Henry.

"I'm trying to say that perhaps we were wrong to kill them. I'm trying to say that if they're fathers of families—that does happen, even with them—their wives and their children are going to miss them. That if they're sons, their mothers are going to cry. And that whether they're fathers, brothers, or sons, their death at our hands will inevitably stoke up hatred against us. I'm suggesting that it's bad business to kill people who may be innocent, and that it's not what we're here for. Once more, all my apologies. I know that since I wasn't in Indochina and I've only been in Algeria a few days, I ought to just listen."

Thus for the first time Captain Julienne said what he felt. Everyone at the table felt a little uncomfortable. Not that they thought he was right.

Julienne was wrong, and he would find it out pretty quick. The *fellagha* are not, more's the pity, beings apart, marked with a cross on the forehead. The *fellagha* are anyone, anywhere. To get a real one you have to round up—or to kill—four or five, at least. Or to give up hunting the *fellagha*. But, in that case, what are we doing in Algeria?

"My dear sir," said Martin, addressing Julienne with a condescending but friendly manner, "you're right, a hundred per cent right—in theory. Unfortunately, in practice you'll find that you're faced with a choice. Either you consider *a priori* that every Arab, in the country, in the street, in a passing truck, is innocent until proved guilty—and allow me to tell you that if that's your attitude you'll get your men bumped off, the *fellagha* will be cocks of the walk, and, as for you, you'll be transferred immediately because the parents of the conscripts you'll get killed won't like it and will write to their deputies that you're a butcher—or you do your duty honorably, which is to say you put the *fellagha* out of commission and look after our men the best you can. In that case, there's only one way: treat every Arab as a suspect, a possible *fellagha*, a potential terrorist—because that, my dear sir, is the truth. And don't come back at me with words like *justice* and *charity*. They have nothing to do with it. I don't say they don't exist: I say all that's not in the same boat. You can talk about that in Paris with the politicians who got us into this mess. But once you're here, raising problems of conscience—and presuming the innocence of possible murderers—is a luxury that costs dear, that costs men, my dear sir, young men, innocent too, our men. I don't think you'll need more than a fortnight to see it."

Outside, in the nighttime silence of the curfew, only the abrupt sound of short bursts from automatic arms, near or far, beat a regular rhythm. The armored patrol that scoured the country in the evening had made it a rule never to come back without "emptying its magazines." Everything that stirs is suspect.

Everyone was watching Captain Julienne. His black eyes, under their heavy, graying eyebrows, wandered around the table. Doubtless he felt that he had spoken a little rashly; he was alone.

Chapter Two

1/ We had been marching for at least two hours in silence, not seeing a thing. The long Indian file was strung out over nearly a mile.

The trucks had dropped us on the road that mounts from the village of Tala Youssef toward the first ridge of the mountains that look down on the Mitidja. On top, at the Abbey of Saint Geneviève, the road stops, and a series of tracks fans out. A thousand-odd men, coming from all the units near the sector, had been deposited there in successive waves between one and three in the morning.

In the pitch-dark night the companies had been dispatched forward, in order of their serial numbers, to their jumping-off points. The jumping-off points on the mountainside formed a huge circle, which had been described on the map around three villages that had to be surrounded before daybreak.

The bolt of the trap was supplied, along the valley road down below, by the armor.

Captain Julienne lifted his arm to order a halt, and everyone imitated him so as to be seen by the man behind. From one of the deep pockets that American battle-dress trousers have at about knee height he fished out his map.

"Got a flashlight?"

A shadowy form handed him a flashlight with a blue glass, and he directed its halo on three points ticked in red: the *douars*, which, if our position was right, ought to be now between us and the road.

Behind us, making the most of the halt, the long file was sitting down or stretching out in the ditch. Canteens of weak coffee—the only drink Julienne permitted as long as the operation lasted—were being passed from hand to hand.

There was a sound of hurried steps in the undergrowth.

The shadows around us jumped up and trained their weapons in the direction of the noise.

"Who goes there?" came simultaneously from three hoarse voices, which were trying to be heard—but not too far.

"Don't be a stupid bastard. It's me—Bunny!"

With a single bound, so as not to prolong the uncertainty, Sergeant Baral was out of the bushes. Everyone in the regiment called him Bunny because of the peculiar shape of his ears and because he was popular. He was not alone: with the barrel of his tommy-gun he was pushing another shadow in front of him, and as it drew closer it resolved itself into a young Arab in a torn shirt. He was a kid, fourteen or fifteen, and he had an insolent look.

"He's a lookout—I nabbed him as he was rushing down the hill toward the first village. I was a little lower than him, and he didn't see me, and I sent him rolling as he went past. He was moving damn quick, the kid."

"Shall I take charge of him?" said a huge shadow in a voice as clear-cut as the threat it implied.

"No!" interrupted Julienne, holding up his arm to stop the lieutenant who was moving rapidly toward the Arab. And after a second's silence that seemed an eternity, he added in a lower tone: "I'll do it myself."

Julienne was never taken unawares. He had decided before leaving that if this sort of work became necessary, he would neither give an order for it nor allow it to be done in his name: he preferred to take it on himself.

This was the fifth "operation" he had been out on in the fortnight since he had come to the regiment. He knew by now what were the problems, always the same ones, that presented themselves in these standard encirclements.

The operation had been decided on in the late afternoon of the previous day, when the sector staff had received information about the murder that had been committed near Tala Youssef.

The circumstances of the crime were a little worrisome. About seven in the morning an Arab peasant, Mansour Abdallah, one of the few Arab municipal councilors who had not yet resigned, had seen an old man approaching him, bent, hobbling, draped in the sort of great white *kachabia* that can easily cover the face. He was leaning on a knotty stick—a sort of beggar. This old man had calmly come up to him, said: "Good morning, Mansour!" and had then killed him.

Immediately, dispensing with his stick and *kachabia*, the beggar had revealed himself as an athletic man of about thirty. Two farm laborers who had been working in the field with Mansour had dropped their implements and joined the murderer, following a little in the rear to cover his retreat. All three had then made a dash for the road, where a car had just arrived to pick them up, and made off in the direction of Maison Carrée. Now, the two laborers were police informers in one of the villages near Brahim; the murderer, from the description Mansour gave before he died, was a young local football star who between games lived in another village near by; and, finally, the car had been found in an alley of a third village.

These three mountain villages, as quiet as they were poverty-stricken, had suddenly taken on a new light since the day before, so the encirclement operation had been ordered.

Julienne, then, had assumed the job of making the lookout talk. It was an urgent business. By their very nature, these lookouts are invaluable informers—if they can be made to speak. They are not real members of the *maquis*, but they act as its antennae and may know where the others are.

The *maquisards* post these lookouts on heights around

the villages where they are resting up or eating, with orders to give the alarm at the least sign of danger. They choose sporting types, usually boys who are not yet old enough to carry arms but who welcome a chance to take part in the great adventure. Every night, all over Algeria, guard is being mounted around suspect villages by this legion of kids, who are not going to school any more.

The least a lookout can know is to which house in which village he must give the alarm. That information must be pried out of him. The operation may depend on it. The lookout knows it, too: it is not easy to make him talk.

Julienne came back toward us. He had obtained the information.

One of the first houses of the village, already distinguishable through the mist that was diluting the shades of night, was, according to the lookout, a *maquis* supply point. That was where we would start.

It was still twenty minutes before H-hour.

"Set up tactical HQ here and make the radio contacts," said Julienne to a second lieutenant who was operational assistant.

The radio communications began—a background music that is being played all over Algeria and opens the door of the new day on the watchful silence of the encirclements.

"Hello, Red. Cardinal here. Are you receiving me? What is your position? Over!"

"Hello, Blue. Cardinal here. Are you receiving me? What is your position? Over!"

"Hello, Green . . ."

One after another we heard the voices of Red, Blue, Green, Orange—the voices of our comrades who were emerging from the night and locating themselves. On this broad mountainside, where the *mechtas* stood out through gaps in the layer of mist which clung to the ground, nothing was stirring. Only by their radio replies could we guess the positions of our invisible detachments, hiding in the folds of the terrain, crouching in the bushes: they knew the techniques of their job thoroughly now.

A quarter of an hour more.

Julienne sat down on the bank and took a sandwich out of his pocket. Munching it with relish, he looked in turn at the huge bowl in front of us, the three motionless villages of wattle and daub, the Arab kid, his face swollen, who was sleeping in a ditch now, and the outstretched radio antennae.

"What a bastardly game!"

Julienne stretched his long arms toward the sky, over his big, round, gray head, and yawned. I did not know whether he was talking about this monotonous work or the hours of sleep which our midnight departure had deprived us of.

It was H-hour.

Julienne got up. "Message from Cardinal to all detachments: 'You will move off for the operation in three minutes and march on your objectives. Keep me informed. Prisoners will be assembled at the end of the operation on the football field by the road.' End of message. Send it out."

While the second lieutenant repeated the instructions over the set and noted the successive "very goods," the gray light around us became clear, the nearer silhouettes turned into faces and acquired names; little brown dots emerged from the undergrowth and began to advance slowly, on three separate axes, toward the *mechtas*.

A humming filled the whole basin and in a moment was over us. Five fighters, the air cover sent by Algiers, were arriving, in case they were needed for the operation. Behind them, slower and lower, flew a Piper Cub observation plane that would provide liaison between the ground command and the fighters. It was the regular scenario, whose overwhelming superfluity had long ago ceased to astonish us.

Julienne was on his toes. These operations held no surprises for him now, but this time there was a vital difference:
he was in command. Everything that would be done today
would be done in his name. Each of these men was his representative; it was for him that every tommy-gun would be
firing. He was everywhere and must answer for everything: he
was responsible. His feelings bore no relation to his memories, recent as they were, of the other encirclements. Today,
for the first time since he had been here, he was personally
living the war.

It was twelve years, almost to the day, since that had last
happened to him. That had been on the beach near Ravol,
on a day as lovely as this, when he had landed with his commando from the amphibian craft of the De Lattre army,
which had sailed from Algeria. In the France-Germany campaign he had been wounded three times. The last wound
had messed up quite a lot of things in his inside, and had
prevented him from going out to Indochina. Since then
Julienne had never had the occasion to command a unit in
action.

The muted echo of a couple of shots, which might have
come from a distant shotgun, reached our ears. Julienne
raised his binoculars. Daybreak had given us a clear view
over the whole scene of operations. The line of brown dots
which was moving toward the highest village had stopped.

Julienne turned to the second lieutenant squatting by
the radio. "Ask Green in person if the shots were fired in his
sector."

Green was a detachment of the third battalion under
the command of Company Sergeant-Major Gambert, an experienced man who had served in Korea. "Green" was the
radio code name for the section, and "Green in person"
meant Gambert.

He replied that the shots had indeed been fired at his

forward line, and that one of his men had a nasty leg wound. The house from which the firing seemed to come was at the northwest corner of the group of *mechtas*, near a donkey tethered in a field—which "Cardinal" should be able to see from where he was.

Julienne identified the house through his binoculars. The kid, who was still sleeping, worn out by his night of watching and his shock in the small hours, had told him the truth.

Usually the heavy-footedness of the encirclement operations gives the wanted *maquisards* all the time they need to get away. All one finds is accomplices, and sometimes munitions. But it does happen that armed rebels are caught in the net. Then they wait till our line has closed in to point-blank range before firing at our men.

Gambert asked for Cardinal "in person" on the radio. Julienne picked up the headphones.

"My forward line's held up. If I go on, I may have two or three other fellows knocked out before I get to the house with the donkey. I suggest that I go on alone, with a little commando of three men, and take it from the rear, with grenades. I'm waiting for your orders. Over."

Julienne knew Company Sergeant-Major Gambert. He was a peculiar case. He was one of the group of men who had been sent to our regiment by the "patriotic" militia— Volunteers of the French Union, Biaggists, and so forth. He was the biggest and bulkiest of the lot—a former army boxing champion.

Demobilized after the Korean campaign, he had scraped out a living in various jobs that had meant little to him. His only passion was politics: he claimed to be a "nationalist" and hunted down "defeatists" with a group of strong-arm men he had gathered around him.

The day I had first met him, on another operation, he

had accosted me in a tone that was both respectful and provocative: "I hope, sir, that I shall have my photo in *L'Express* again when I get back from Algeria."

I was exceedingly surprised. In the first place, I had absolutely no recollection of his face. It is true that I do not know by heart all the photos that have ever appeared in the paper. In the second place, the undisguised innuendo was astonishing: it was the first time that an NCO of the regiment had deliberately and openly confounded my position in civilian life with my job in the army. Who was this company sergeant-major?

After making my position quite clear to him that day in the bluntest possible fashion, I had no more difficulty in my official relations with Company Sergeant-Major Gambert. He was straight, and he approached his military duties in Algeria with an intelligent single-mindedness that soon made him conspicuous.

"Stay where you are. I'll give you my answer in a moment."

Julienne put down the microphone and examined the position of Gambert's line in relation to the village and the house from which the shots had been fired. Nothing was stirring. Doubtless taken by surprise by the encirclement, and pinned down since one of their neighbors had branded the whole village with the rebel mark, the inhabitants of the group of *mechtas* remained invisible.

Gambert's idea made sense. If he went on alone with a little commando, there would be very little extra risk, and he might silence the house. If the whole line was ordered to advance, more of our men might be knocked out, and then nobody could prevent their creating havoc in all the houses— that one and the others.

Julienne was just about to give the green light to Gambert's commando over the microphone. Then a new voice came out of the radio, a stranger's interrupted by interference which showed that it came from above. It must be the Piper Cub, or perhaps the Bell helicopter of the army staff which was now also circling right over the field of the operation.

"Hello, Cardinal. Hello . . . hel . . . Cricket here. Are you receiving me? Over."

"Hello, Cricket. Cardinal here. I'm receiving you two fifths. Speak slowly. Over."

"Hello, Cardinal. I want . . . al . . . in person for Big Soup . . . son . . . Over."

"Cardinal in person here. I'm waiting for Big Soup. Over."

Julienne pulled out of his pocket the OBT: a mimeographed sheet of paper on which the radio code for the day was set out. Big Soup? That was the general from headquarters who was in over-all command of the three arms—infantry, armor, and air—of the combined operation.

All over Algeria, when discussions are begun in a mess, you will hear the same story: "Generals are stupid bastards."

The reality is not quite so simple. Generals are generals. Now, promotion from the rank of colonel to that of general in the army today is apt to be the result of politics. If candidates for general rank (colonels sufficiently senior to become generals) want to get their stars, they become clients of some Minister. There are exceptions, and these are as respected as they are rare. But, taken as a whole, our army, whose body is still healthy, is putrefying from the head down; intrigues and faction fights are gaining on it.

What is more, generals like commanding. That is natural. But a general's command—that is, a command in which the scale of the forces employed and of the operational plan call for a commander senior to colonel—is a pretty big affair. Thus, if generals are to command without losing cast, it is necessary to put on operations that look as if they were large-scale. Now, there are a lot of generals in Algeria who neither want to mark time—which would jeopardize their reputation and their promotion—nor, it stands to reason, to go back to a captain's insignia to do a job of work. That is the reason for the number of operations put on every week regardless of expense. Moreover, these operations must not be phony: there must be results—more results than the other generals have achieved.

No one knows better than the army itself the harm that is being done to the army of Algeria by some of its generals.[1]

Julienne was filled with apprehension. If Big Soup was sticking his finger into the pie, where were things going to end? It was useless to worry, of course: the moment generals appear on the horizon in those fascinating dragonflies of helicopters, captains become machines to carry out orders.

The Bell was by now directly above us, hovering at a height of about three hundred feet, to make conversation easier.

"Hello, Cardinal, Big Soup in person here. Why is Green's line held up? Over."

"Shots have been fired on our men from the house at the northwest corner of the village. I'm going to send in a little commando to silence the house. Over."

There were more shots, followed by several bursts of fire. The house had opened up again, and our men were replying from the thicket where they had stopped. There was still no movement in the village.

"Cardinal: if the house has opened fire, I order you to suspend any further ground attack. I'm going to call in our artillery support, and then the air if necessary. My instruc-

[1] I had the good fortune in Algeria to meet and get to know a general whose humanity, modesty, and character compel respect. The example he and one or two others showed enabled one to gauge the distance that, unhappily, separates the exception from the rule.

tions are: pull back your troops till your front line is at least two hundred yards from the outskirts of the village. Is that clear? Over."

Sometimes at moments like this a question would flash across Julienne's mind: wasn't this the time to take the plunge—to challenge bluntly the all-powerful hierarchy with his individual reaction, to tell a general just what he thought of him, to disobey orders, and to leave the army?

In these sudden fits of temper he saw himself, in a matter of seconds, tramping the roads as a resigned ex-regular officer, proclaiming to the people in every market place of France that their army, the pride of the nation, was on the way to becoming a sinister masquerade in the hands of a few climbers and a host of halfwits.

Then he recovered his calm and looked at things more soberly. What was an ex-regular captain? He was not worth a straw. He was nothing at all. Where would sending in his papers get him? Surely there must be some other way of crying out and of acting. He was not the only one. So many of his friends, who, like himself, had chosen this splendid career, felt as he did. If they got together and backed one another up, they could surely manage to change things—couldn't they?

Meantime, there were orders to be obeyed.

"Very good," Julienne said simply.

And his words opened the floodgates to the usual absurdity, whose latest performance he was, indeed, probably powerless to stop singlehanded.

A little commando is a captain's weapon. A bombardment is a general's.

Suddenly Julienne saw, rushing up the steep and stony path we were looking down on, an unarmed, uniformed man whose bulk made his speed seem quite a feat. The man went straight for Julienne. It was Gambert.

"What does all this circus mean? Have you gone mad?" Gambert used what breath he had left to shout as loud as he could.

You do not, as a rule, talk that way to a superior officer. And Gambert generally knew how to keep his place, for he was fond of army life. But when he felt something strongly, he did sometimes forget himself. To those who knew him, these outbursts only showed his sincerity.

Julienne understood him. Anyway, he had more important things to think of at the moment than pulling his rank.

"General's orders."

A menacing grimace contorted Gambert's pugilistic features. He was beside himself. Julienne had no desire to let him make a scene in front of the other officers and NCO's gathered at the tactical headquarters.

"Listen, Gambert, go and calm down and then come and talk to me. That's an order."

All the same, Julienne was curious to learn what had put the man of the patriotic militia into such a fury. Probably he was indignant at being deprived of the little commando job he had proposed: he needed only one more mention in dispatches to have a right to the military medal.

When Gambert came back, his face was less flushed, but his jaw was set. He sat down beside Julienne without a word. After a series of deep breaths, Gambert said in a steady voice: "I've had enough, sir. I'm going back to France. I'm going to ask you to put me down for leave pending demobilization as of tomorrow."

"Why?"

"This sort of thing disgusts me."

"Me, too—but why you?"

"Don't be impertinent. I mean what I say: I've had enough. I came here with the others to try and keep Algeria—not to smash it up. What we're doing doesn't make any sense.

We might be living in a Communist caricature. **Of course** we run fewer risks this way. But we'd run fewer risks still if we withdrew our troops to France. Because, as far as saving Algeria goes, we're going full tilt into the bloody mess: we're turning all the inhabitants into *fellagha*. For one rebel we kill, we're making twenty ready to replace him. I'm getting out. I didn't come here for this."

Julienne was called to the radio post. Elements of Red had entered the second village. They'd found ten grenades and three sacks of shotgun cartridges in a *mechta*. They'd rounded up all the men of the *mechta*.

Julienne repeated the story to Gambert.

"More phony stuff," Gambert said. "Last night I saw the CO of the *chasseurs* giving the orders himself to the sergeant of Red. He told him: 'I'm fed up with the bastards of the village where you're going. This time they've got to be thrown into the jug. They're certain to have some arms hidden up there. If you don't find any, *you'll plant this*, and you'll find it later.' He gave him the grenades and the cartridges—to be certain there'd be no slip-up. Personally, I don't give a damn: if they're real bastards, any trick's good enough. But when I see all this, I ask myself where we're going to."

Julienne had a furious desire to smash everything in sight.

Everything?

Perhaps the arms Red had found were the ones their CO had ordered put there; but perhaps not. Yesterday's murder was not phony. Nor were the shots that had just wounded our men. Nor was the ambush that had almost cost his driver's life on the road to headquarters on Sunday night. Not everything was phony—far from it.

And even in the things that could not be excused, one had to make a further distinction. The business of Mauré the other day, murdering the workers in the truck, was a blind absurdity for which nobody was responsible. All the same, five innocent men were dead, and the last Arab workers had left the mine. The officer's orders to his men on the "fixed" search were the last straw. All the same, the village in question quite certainly (Julienne knew it, too) sheltered terrorists, who never left anything around just because they were so well organized.

Perhaps there was nothing to do but wash one's hands of it: probably Gambert was right.

But even Gambert's decision was phony: he would stay.

There were orders to be given. Radio queries had started to flow in again. Eighty prisoners from the other villages had already been rounded up on the football field. The fighters were strafing—machine-gunning from treetop height—the surrounding woods in case fugitives had taken refuge there. Big Soup was asking Cardinal the number of *fellagha*—by which the general meant "Arabs"—killed and captured: it was time to send the first communiqué to General Headquarters at Algiers. Elements of Blue who had come over the hilltop were turning up around the headquarters: they brought with them, in sacks, all the chickens they had looted in the villages and displayed them to their comrades with pride. "We're going to eat better stuff than the ration tonight, boys."

Anyone could see the absurdity of it all, the balance sheet of such an operation: the area "rotten" for months, the exodus of the population, hatred of France distributed by the fistful. Once a certain threshold is reached, no doubt, any individual will is powerless to act or even to express itself. What had Julienne done today to set things right, what had he even tried to do? Nothing, absolutely nothing.

It was noon. Our men, scattered all around, bowed down with fatigue, unshaved since the previous day, were awaiting the order for the end of the operation. The canteens had long been empty. The heat of the midday sun was transforming our detachments into a *harka*. The spectacle against the background of newly made ruins, framed by the columns of smoke which were mounting around the basin from ricks and from crops, made Julienne physically sick.

The general's helicopter circled above us for the last time and transmitted a message for Julienne: "Tell your men that I've been extremely satisfied with their conduct on this operation. All our objectives have been attained. You will send to me at Algiers a list of the men you recommend for decorations. Keep me posted on the state of the wounded. Good work, and good-by."

Captain Julienne, who had been a regular officer for fifteen years, listened as the radio repeated this message for him. His eyes were staring straight in front of him, and his fists were clenched in the pockets of his battle-dress trousers.

2/   It will be a long time before I forget the details of the afternoon when I met Major Marcus.

He was a lighthouse of a man. You will find them everywhere in the army of Algeria, though they are not so many: one or two per sector. They are men who are determined, wherever they may be, to stop the flood of insanity and to hold fast by their own means.

Whether they are in mountain posts, or in mobile units, or in the Special Pacification Sections, the SAS, what unites them is their common resolution to fight with all their force against the resistless mesh of circumstances which is making for a complete breach with the Moslems.

As long as such men remain, the last light will not have gone out. Their activities may be limited and local, but they are symbolic. Their names are repeated from one village to another, and signify hope. They are the lay priests of our African Middle Ages.

Marcus. I knew the name, but not the man.

The quarters of his unit were not far from ours, but Marcus was almost never there. He would be tramping over mountain tracks with the section of Moslem *goumiers* he had trained himself. As often as not, he slept with the locals in the *mechtas,* so as never to break contact by day or by night. The command of his unit of dragoons he left to a second-in-command.

A few days after the last encirclement operation Julienne took us over to the dragoons' quarters. He hoped that Marcus would not be out on a round. He had not yet had an opportunity to see Marcus since the latter had arrived in the area. Julienne was not pressed: there was time. But once he had made up his mind to leave Algeria, he had to talk to Marcus.

Marcus was in his quarters. He was working—or, as the army of Africa puts it, "spoiling paper"—in a sort of caretaker's lodge of a luxurious local villa. In the yard were one or two officers and the Arabs of his personal guard. The unit's quarters were opposite, on the other side of the road.

He was as pleased as he was surprised to see Julienne entering the little whitewashed room that was his office. Although they had been contemporaries at the military college, they met but rarely. Such was the luck of the French army, with all its tribulations.

"Marcus," Julienne said, "I arrived in Algeria last month. I've been working with the infantry regiment next door, a unit like the rest, well-commanded on the whole and composed of honest reservists. I've taken part in the day-to-day grind. I've seen enough here to be convinced that what they're making us do here is leading straight to the loss of Algeria—not to speak of our honor as Frenchmen. I've no need to spin a long yarn, you know it all better than I; you see what I want to say. . . . I'd believed that with honest goodwill one could influence the way things are going a little: it's a Boy Scout's idea. I'm packing up. Before I go, though, I've come to see you, for one chapter in my education is missing: is it really the same everywhere in Algeria? And why are you still here?"

Marcus, who always took serious things seriously, and who had known Julienne for twenty years, recognized the occasion for what it was. This was not just a friendly conversation: a conscience was at war with itself. He did not say anything. He got up from his chair, went over to a white wood chest of drawers at the other end of his little room, and rummaged among the papers there. He took out a folder and came back and sat down at his table. Turning its pages, he began to talk, slowly.

"I haven't been *all* over Algeria—but nearly. In nine months I've worked with fifteen different units. I know what you want to say, and I understand your question. The answer is: yes. We're behaving like idiots almost everywhere."

Marcus started to walk up and down the room. He stopped in front of the window overlooking the yard, and stared at his men who were repairing a truck. Then he turned around abruptly and looked steadily at me.

"You who are a journalist, you ought to see that all this is made known. We are a silent service, and when we want to talk, we haven't the means to communicate. But you are here, so take advantage of it. You've got nothing to lose. Tell people what's happening. After all, it's got to be told."

"I'm not here as a journalist."

"Of course. But afterward?"

"Afterward I'll do what I can. But you must know that the army in Algeria has been turned into a national taboo to which you can only pay compliments. Anyone who criticized its methods would immediately be suspected of the darkest designs. We're in a vicious circle: soldiers, whose opinion on the way the army's being used would carry great weight, can't make their opinion known; civilians, when they can talk, are discredited. The taboo can afford to sleep soundly."

Marcus fixed his eyes on the ceiling. A longish silence followed. Julienne was the first to break it.

"So, really, it's the same everywhere, we're carrying out an upside-down pacification. With our own hands we're turning what started off as a rebellion into a revolutionary war. Hidden behind the communiqués, with their daily dozens of '*fellagha* killed and arms captured,' there's this staggering fact: the entire Arab population is joining the resistance against us. That's a pretty kettle of fish. But the bewildering thing isn't this vicious circle: everyone knows about that. It's that everything goes on as if we hadn't learned a thing. Aren't there any high-ups, civilians or soldiers, who can see that day by day we are building up the classic conditions for a disaster under the pretense of maintaining order?"

"There are," said Marcus. "More than you'd think. It's not stupidity that's destroying us, it's cowardice. They understand, but they don't turn a hair. People are lying, Julienne, they're lying from the top to the bottom of the ladder. Lying has become second-nature here. People lie so much that they don't know they're doing it. You lie from a sense of duty, you see. Once you've got that far, there's no way out.

"I'll give you an example. Last month I was in the famous area of the 'reconciliations,' the shopwindow of pacification, where they wanted to hold the first elections. To publicize the fact that the area had been pacified, they built a great new road through the district where fighting had only just stopped and then staged a grand opening. There were ribbons to cut, champagne, photographers, journalists, officials from Algiers, and so on—on a Thursday morning. That very afternoon there were five ambushes—do you hear, five!

There'd never been so many. And they cut our convoys on the new road to pieces. There was an urgent call for helicopters to evacuate the wounded—that's how I heard it, through the pilots. Then what did they do? Not only was this news withheld from the press, but the articles about the 'pacified area' had to be published regardless. Well, maybe there was some sense in that. But *even the Minister* didn't know the facts: they didn't dare tell him.

"You say the Government's feeding a lot of bull to the country? Fair enough, but the generals and the prefects are telling lies to the Ministers, the captains and the mayors are telling lies to the generals and the prefects, and so it goes on *ad infinitum*. When a dirty bit of work is done in my regiment by some of my men on an operation, do you think I'm told? Not on your life. They cover it up 'between buddies.' If I hear of it, it's only by chance. The example comes from the top, and it's contaminated the whole pyramid, right to the very bottom. It's common knowledge: there are the things you can say and—the others.

"And all this goes on, naturally, in front of the Moslems who are everywhere, who are watching us, listening to us, reading our papers. . . . You can see where it's all leading."

A company sergeant-major knocked at the door, came in, and saluted Marcus. "Could I see you for a moment, sir?" The man looked anxious and distressed.

"What's it about, Bonnard?"

"Trouble, sir. I've got to talk to you at once."

Our presence there obviously dismayed him.

"Go ahead," said Marcus. "I've nothing to hide from these officers. What's wrong?"

"There've been three desertions this morning, sir. I've just realized it. Ben Ammar, Hocine, and Hammoud. Nobody knows where they've gone, but it's desertion, all right.

They tried to get another man to go with them, but he refused and ended up by coming and telling me. I reported it immediately to Lieutenant Bousquine so that he could come and see you. He didn't want to. He told me he was ashamed. He preferred it to be me."

"Thank you, Bonnard. Stay with the other men of the special company and tell me later how they take it. Have two jeeps and two Dodges standing by to leave in an hour. Tell Lieutenant Bousquine to be in my office in twenty minutes, ready to come with me."

The company sergeant-major saluted again and went out, relieved. The burden was on someone else's shoulders now.

We waited in silence for Marcus to decide whether he wanted to talk to us. We knew that this specialized company was the apple of his eye, an instrument he had forged himself. He had incorporated eighty Algerian Moslem *goumiers* into his regiment, with whom he went out and "made contact" with the people of the remotest mountain *douars*. That was his way of reacting; that was his own kind of pacification, the real kind.

For his second-in-command he had chosen a Moslem officer, Lieutenant Haouch Bousquine. The only Frenchman in the company was Company Sergeant-Major Bonnard, who was there to train the men. Marcus's reputation and his moral authority were not based only on the ideas he expressed, but on the small fraction of them that he succeeded in translating into hard fact: the success of his experiment of nomadization, of penetrating the Arab world and living among the people.

"It's not the first time," Marcus said. "There are about two or three desertions a month. You've either got to take the risk or give up working with Moslems. The thing that matters every time is the others: you've got to talk to them for hours and get them into action at once. Otherwise, they'll take off, too."

Marcus would be on the road again this evening, then. We had only a few more minutes with him.

"Look, old man," said Julienne, "I hate taking your time when you've got urgent business to see to, but I probably won't see you again. I'm asking to be relieved tomorrow, and I'm going back to France. What you've told us confirms what I said this morning: there's nothing to be done—unless one's got the talent and the means for a singlehanded effort. As you seem to have. When it comes to me, the only thing I can hold to is a refusal to be an accomplice."

Marcus slowly shook his square head, so surprising on top of his angular body, and stared up at the ceiling again as if hunting for words that would express his feelings accurately.

"You mustn't go, Julienne. I'd like to try and tell you why. . . . I feel really deeply that we've absolutely got to stay here with all our strength, and with the best of ourselves. . . .

"If you wish, pacification is, in a sense, finished. Mind you, it wasn't impossible. But we'd have had to go about it in quite a different way. An army as big as this, straight from France, could have been an instrument of reconciliation with the ordinary people here. What the Arabs hated was the colonial set-up; they didn't really hate France. The army should have been independent of the colonial set-up, it should have remained separate from the rottenness of the administration, from the settlers, the policemen, the mayors, from everything that the colonial attitude has represented for a century now and that's going to go by the board. The army could have done it: if it had acted as a referee, it could have changed the nature of the problem to be solved. It did the very opposite. Everything's going on now as if this huge army were here simply to protect the privileges of a handful of our fellow Frenchmen. And of course the army has become racialist. Pacification, isolating the rebellion and stamping it out—that's all over. And if it were only a question of that, you'd be right, we'd probably have nothing more to do here. But wait a moment. . . ."

Marcus talked in a voice that was like himself: sober and unexpected. His face and his gestures fused into a curious unity with that voice, and, listening to him, we felt—I still feel it now—a sort of embarrassed eagerness, a disturbing desire to go on listening to him indefinitely, which might almost have been a presentiment. He went on deliberately, as if the only thing in the world that mattered was to convince his friend.

"When we fell down over pacification, by a monstrous piece of stupidity, we let ourselves in, Julienne, for something very much bigger. It just is not possible—mark my words, *not possible*—for an army of five hundred thousand Frenchmen, the biggest that's ever gone overseas, backed by the efforts of the entire country, with all France's resources at its disposal, to stand by indefinitely with folded hands, watching itself being defeated or dishonored. No, this time it's not just the Indochina expeditionary corps that's involved —this time it's the whole country. It would be a disaster that would extend far beyond the business here. It's not a question of the battle of Algeria any more.

"Remember this: what with the reservists, the draftees and regular army men, it's an entire generation that's passing through our hands. We're turning them into moral failures, sometimes into monsters. We could turn them into heroes, or—let's skip the big word—into men. There's no magic formula for it, just example. That's why what you call the single-handed effort is an absolute necessity. It's the last thing that's left to us—but it's the most important. I'm not talking any more of political success—maintaining order, rounding up *fellagha*. I'm talking of what will remain years after Algeria has become a free nation: what was the behavior of half a million young men sent by France into the midst of another race, another people? At the end of the story, at the heart of everything, when all this business is over and amounts to no more than a line in the history books, what shall we read in that line: hate—or love? If countries have a soul, France's soul is here, waiting to be saved.

"This game isn't over yet, you see. It won't be lost or won till the last moment, as long as there are still French soldiers here—and it will be played out by a mere handful of them. Maybe I've written pacification off. But not this— and it's a hundred times more important.

"That's why you're going to stay, Julienne. To play your irreplaceable part, like the others, in this battle."

Company Sergeant-Major Bonnard came in again. His face was as anxious as it had been the first time—worse, even. This time Marcus had a shock when he looked at him.

"What is it, Bonnard?"

"There's been a catastrophe, sir!"

"Well, what is it? Come on, speak up!"

"The deserters, sir. They've got away with two light machine guns and the magazines. It's a catastrophe!"

It was. You can, in a pinch, put up with two or three desertions a month. But you certainly cannot if at the same time you lose those murderous weapons, made for guerrilla warfare and worth their weight in gold to the rebels. Every machine gun lost makes it certain that someday, on some road or other, one of our convoys is going to be wiped out. On another level, it means, too, the certainty of an explosion by the authorities. A perfectly justifiable explosion, for it is estimated that the rebels have got from the French army about three times as many arms as they have received from the outside. They are living off us.

Marcus was more than worried. He had to map out a line of action at once. If he did not run down the deserters and their weapons, his experiment was sunk. The criticisms and the jealousies that had accumulated around him would unleash a storm he could no longer stand up under. And the very harshness of his constantly and quite openly expressed views on the hidebound methods of our military machine as a whole would count against him. He had only a few hours in which to act. If night fell before he had caught up with the fugitives, he would be lost. How was he to lay hands on them—an encirclement operation? Nothing doing. He could think of only one means: to make use of his influence with the local Moslems he knew. He would go and see them with his men, and hope they would tip him off as to which way the deserters had gone.

He had been talking a few moments before of the ordeal by truth which the country faced. Now he was facing his own.

While Marcus and his Moslem second-in-command, Bousquine, were completing preparations for their patrol, the CO of our regiment, Lieutenant Colonel Espanieul, joined us. Just back from Paris, he wanted, as usual, to give us a play-by-play account of his running battle with the Ministers. He invited us to dinner at the fashionable Algiers hotel, the Saint Georges, where every night soldiers, journalists, deputies over to "see the war," police informers, and businessmen meet in a great circus.

Julienne, whose head was in a whirl, had nothing against a little relaxation. And the colonel had a way with him.

Marcus, equipped for a long trip, jumped in beside his chauffeur and waved a friendly good-by to us. Followed by

Bousquine in another jeep, and by two truckloads of his *goumiers*, he set out toward the south, toward a fate he could not guess.

3/ Dinner at the Saint Georges is like the Legion of Honor: you've got to have it. To be in the swim, you must be seen at the Saint Georges.

This well-planned hotel, built in tropical style on the heights a little above the Governor's Summer Palace, has become the same kind of swarming crossroads that the terrace of the Aletti was in the center of Algiers, after the Allied landings of 1942.

But "dining at the Saint Georges" is not a mere matter of getting into a car, driving to the hotel, and sitting down at a table. You have to know people, and be known. Everything depends on your contacts: on the news you pick up or let drop; on your ability to size up the difference in the viewpoint or the mood of this or that important figure as compared with the week before; on that subtle indication of the feel of things which you have to gauge, and which gives you the official temperature of the war. No, dining at the Saint Georges is not for everyone.

That particular evening we entered the smart dining-room under the best possible auspices. You might say that Lieutenant Colonel Robert Espanieul was the uncrowned king of the Saint Georges. The reasons why he reigned over the milieu with such nonchalance were many: the chief one was that he was not part of it. If he made an impression on the hostesses of Algiers, it was not because he had cultivated a better line of small talk than his rivals. On the contrary, he owed it to his brutish appearance and his obvious liking for trouble—in more than one form. When you saw him at dinner in the big dining-room, you told yourself that two hours later he would almost certainly be heading a night patrol at forced-march pace in the southern mountains—or seducing one of the few pretty women in Algiers who are worth the effort. One or the other: you could be almost certain of it.

Dining with him was a real pleasure. Every table became a story.

"Well, old buddy, how did the trip to Paris go? What are they saying over there? Have they got it into their heads what it's all about? They're not going to let us down, I hope! . . ."

An impressive-looking man, with that type of modern face whose intelligence seems to have congealed a little under the layer of meals dictated by the demands of public relations, with trim hair and well-cared-for nails, laid one hand warmly on Espanieul's shoulder and with the other indolently acknowledged our presence.

Espanieul did not lift his eyes from his plate, and continued to eat as he answered:

"Say, you! Have you any objection to not using my name to keep your shop going?"

The impressive-looking man could take it—he looked as if he were used to this sort of thing—but it is never very pleasant. He did his best to summon up a smile as he looked at us, as if to share our amusement at the funny things the colonel *would* say.

"Good," Espanieul said at once, without giving the man a chance to get a word in, "go and make your pile where you like—but not here. I didn't come to Algeria for that."

He continued: "Would you like some wine, Julienne?"

By this time the man had flushed a little. He murmured some sort of getaway phrase and extricated himself as quietly as he could.

Espanieul went on, for our benefit. "He's got nerve, that fellow! D'you know who he is? Singer. He's a bigwig in his party and holds forth endlessly on the greatness of 'French Algeria' at every Congress. His hand on his heart and the flag draped round him: 'Can you see me giving up Algeria, gentlemen? Never!' And of course the usual line about 'the heroism of our wonderful boys.' D'you see what I mean? He does it so well that I believed him. When I turned up here, he was all over me, pleasant, attentive, all eagerness to help. Did I need anything for my regiment, was everything going well? I mentioned casually that we were hard up for everything, particularly trousers. D'you know what he did? The next day he sent a telegram to the Minister, *in my name*, asking for three thousand pairs of trousers of a special cloth to be made at his factory near Algiers. He was out of luck: I know the Minister, and he told me about it. Since then I've gathered that Singer counts on his contacts at the Saint Georges to keep his shop going. Everyone knows it here— there are plenty of others in the same racket. In Paris he's still a hero of French Algeria. As far as I'm concerned, he's had it."

The impressive-looking man, whom I recognized now as one of the big shots of Algerian political life, was hard at work at a neighboring table. He was already cooking up another scheme.

Julienne was entranced. He looked around this big aquarium with enchantment: everything in it amused him. He didn't give a thought either to the morning's operation or to the new problems that Marcus had posed. He had the priceless gift of being able to relax, to empty his mind by throwing himself into the delightful diversion of an idle hour.

And how could one fail to be impressed by the feeling of being right in the middle of things—a feeling that is always created by the presence of people who "count"? A whole galaxy of them was all around us. The all-powerful

Senator who owns the finest estates in Algeria, in serious conversation with two deputies sent out on an inquiry by the
National Assembly. The political adviser to the Minister
Resident, an important man, eating alone, on a diet. A hero
of Dien-Bien-Phu who had made the covers of several magazines, and two ravishing women who had come to spend the
week-end with their draftee husbands, in the middle of a
group of delighted officers. The very Parisian chairman of the
Departmental Council, whose picture had appeared that
morning on the front page of the *Journal d'Alger* with a re-
frigerator presented to a regiment of reservists by a charita-
ble organization. And in that corner over on the right, the
commander-in-chief in person, quiet and serious; the figures
flitting from table to table did not dream of disturbing him,
consecrated as he was by the eminence of his position and
by his lovely silver hair.

It was only an impression, of course. The real events of
history are rarely hatched where the celebrities of the moment are to be seen. Just as many people could have been
seen in the same dining-room three years before, at the time
when, in an anonymous *mechta* of the Aurès Mountains,
Messrs. Ben Bella and Ouamrane, both quite unknown, were
sketching out childish plans for a preposterous insurrection.
And it was the completely unsuspected tension of the coro-
nary artery of a retired general in Washington, and that
alone, which would determine whether one day he or Mr.
Stevenson would find himself in the center of the world between Colonel Nasser and Mr. Ben-Gurion. . . . But, as nobody has a crystal ball that will foretell the future and advise
us which men of today will make tomorrow and are carrying
the seeds of the new world, it is an amusing enough pastime
to watch the celebrities.

"Who is that lovely brunette?" Julienne asked the colonel, making it plain what he was thinking about.

Whether she was a brunette or a blonde, that was in Espanieul's province. Just by looking at him, you couldn't account for his success with women, but it could not be denied. He was of medium height and massively built, and his face was a sort of battlefield: black hair that was always tousled, startling green eyes, a thick and slightly crooked nose with a scar on it. He alternated between being very handsome and very ugly from day to day, and even from one hour to the next. In the presence of a beautiful woman, though, he was always handsome: he lit up from within—as in battle.

The physical attraction that women found in Espanieul would not, in the ordinary course of events, have been a subject of any great interest, or a factor in the present situation. It had become so, however, because of the real *power* over men which that charm gave him.

In the animal universe that the army represents, particularly in wartime, one quite often finds this true. Relations are relations of power, and the physical element predominates. On paper, only rank counts; in fact, the real status men hold is based on the degree of their virility. Every form of virility counts. Strength comes first, whether it is a matter of settling an argument with bare fists or holding out an extra two hours on a night march. Next comes possession of a well-made body and a handsome face, which compel attention and throw a spell over a man's words and deeds (the "physical spell" of the military manuals). Finally, there is the subtlest element, less talked about but far more pervasive than the rest: the almost sexual possession of other men through the medium of women.

The village grocer's wife was a magnificent Algerian woman, swarthy, provocative, self-assured. Two of our NCO's and three officers had taken to doing the shopping themselves, so as to get near the fire. . . . In the end, it was a sergeant from Montpellier who had the pretty grocer's wife. His relations with the three officers were transformed: he had possessed them, physically. They were still his superiors, but he had become their master. On an operation, it was he who gave the orders.

At the end of a few weeks—through a thousand tests of strength, large and small—in any community of men a hierarchy of sexuality is established. Irresistibly this modifies the structure of the community and builds up, behind the unchanged surface, an animal world that dominates.

It is not the fear of death which haunts men in the army, but the fear of being less a man. You never hear anyone say: "Look out, or you'll get yourself knocked off." But a dozen times a day you hear: "If you goof, you'll get hung by the nuts."

Espanieul was exceedingly intelligent, and he had one principal source of confidence: he was the most animal-like of animals. You had only to see his lascivious smile whenever he talked about women.

The brunette was not unknown to him. And it was not her husband with whom she was dining. The husband was a major, somewhere in the south, but she was no longer very fond of him.

"A rather funny thing happened to me with her. . . ."

In our enjoyment of this idle hour in an unaccustomed world we had almost forgotten where we were. We were quite surprised when, threading his way awkwardly through the tables in his camouflaged battle dress, we saw Private Geronimo approaching us.

"I've come to pick you up, sir, and the other officers, too," said Geronimo, standing at attention. "There's been another ambush on the Sakamody road."

"Anyone killed?"

"Twenty dead and some wounded; almost the whole convoy."

"What unit?"

"A dragoon regiment—almost all Moslem soldiers, it seems."

A single question hung in the air. No one could bring himself to ask it. Finally, Espanieul said:

"Who was in command of the convoy?"

"Major Marcus."

"He's dead?"

"No, missing. The other officer's dead: Lieutenant Vousquine, or something like that. . . . The bastards, I'd have given my eyes to be there!"

Julienne got up. Espanieul got up. Together we crossed the dining-room in the direction of our jeeps, which you could see beyond the green plants at the far end of the terrace.

From here to Sakamody, at the best, was an hour and a half. Ninety minutes, then, before we got to that murderous gorge, whose every turn we already knew. At least that long before we reached our comrades who would be already on reconnaissance. Ninety minutes before we would know, perhaps, what had happened to the little man—magnified to full stature by the image our hopes drew of him, in the moonlight sky, on the clouds above the far-off ridge of Sakamody.

4/ Even today I cannot hear that name without a feeling of uneasiness: for me Sakamody, more than any other name, more than Tablat, more than Palestro, more than Batna or Kenchela, holds in its syllables a legendary quality.

The day I heard it for the first time was the day we arrived. In the morning we had disembarked from the *Ville d'Alger*; the same afternoon I found myself, with no intermediate stage—and, what is more, with nothing to eat—in the farmyard of an old and partly abandoned farm to the south of the Mitidja, in charge of a company of infantry.

The CO of our regiment had been told in Paris that we should have a month's training in a training-camp. At Algiers they needed men to guard the isolated farms from which our fellow Frenchmen are being driven by insecurity, by the desertion of their Moslem labor, and by nagging anxiety. The regiment had therefore been dispersed all over the plain so as to sprinkle the area with khaki uniforms. The principal aim was to overawe the rebels: most of our men did not know how to shoot.

We waited for nightfall in this oasis at the end of the world, after a chaotic effort to organize around the grounds a defense system improvised out of what we could find in an old barn. As daylight slowly faded on us, a handful of reservists, our job was to frustrate in any possible way the terrorists who had been burning the crops. It was a new feeling for us. The men on guard duty had nothing to be afraid of: the others joined them, staring into the dark lines of vine plants that ran on to the horizon.

The last rays of the sun imparted a new life to the shadows and handed us over to the unknown.

A man and a woman who were taking a leisurely stroll, enjoying the cool night air, stopped and chatted with us by the little firesteps we had made about a hundred yards from their house. They seemed to get an extraordinary pleasure out of it.

"It's the first time since the emergency that we've been able to take an evening stroll as far as this," the farmer's wife told us. "We just haven't been able to go out. After six in the evening you have to barricade yourself in till the next morning. At nighttime you don't feel as if you were at home any more."

The words filled our reservists at once with self-satisfaction and with fear. France's defense of Algeria, in concrete and visible form, was us, then. It was this quiet stroll that a couple on a farm were at long last able to take. But it was also the night, which we had to dispute with the *fellagha*—for at night, we gathered, the *fellagha* reigned supreme. Was the "front" here? And in what form would they come tonight? The farmer and his wife were bombarded with questions.

Our men were not sleeping. One by one they got up from their improvised palliasses in the old barn and in what used to be the agent's house. They came over to join us, to pick up for themselves the scent of the enemy's presence in the answers the farmer was giving us.

"The bands—they come here, and then they go away. You never know when they may come. Sometimes they'll spend a whole night cutting down the vines or sawing down orange trees. Another time they will set fire to the crops or to a building—and then they make for the mountains, where you can't catch them."

"And where do they go in the mountains?"

The farmer's wife turned around to face a chain of big hills to the south, whose outline was already fading in the half-light. Overwrought and tired, she stretched out her arm and pointed toward one height, as if to call down a well-merited vengeance on the distant spot.

"It's there, their hide-out. . . . It's Sakamody!"

There is nothing left of Sakamody today. Not a single house is standing in those groups of *mechtas* along the roadside. But in the middle of this dead area, the silence of whose abandoned ruins is strangely impressive, we had set up one of our mountain posts and re-christened it Sakamody.

The post is strongly held. But on the road that leads to it, rebel ambushes are frequent and costly: transport is allowed through only under armed escort, and is forbidden after nightfall, except for machine-gun carriers.

Seated beside his driver, his two hands gripping his American rifle firmly, his large shoulders hunched forward, his tousled black hair sticking out from under his beret, Espanieul wouldn't hear of an escort for the last lap of the mountain road on the night of the new ambush: it would only hold us up. But the sentry, a stickler for regulations, kept the barrier down across the road: nothing doing without the armored escort. So we waited for one of the platoons of tanks which from nightfall on do a regular patrol, as they do on all the roads of Algeria in the danger areas.

The ambush had taken place in a valley of Sakamody. Major Henry, who had received the alarm at his headquarters in a radio message, was waiting for us with his men at the scene of the battle—or, rather, of the butchery.

Sixteen brown and four white corpses, naked and neatly mutilated, were laid out on the roadside under one of the earthen banks of the D.R.S. (a public department for soil-conservation and improvement which is trying, as best it can, to carry on its work in Algeria). There were two survivors. One, a Moslem private, had miraculously come through without a scratch. The other was dying: Lieutenant Haouch Bousquine, Marcus's second-in-command.

The drama was the oldest kind of trick, and it had been over in a flash.

Marcus was heading toward Tablat, on the track of his deserters and their machine guns. The vehicle in the lead had passed the first D.R.S. bank and was almost alongside the second when the collective murder at point-blank range (which might be the definition of any well-armed and well-laid ambush) began.

Two machine guns, one firing from the front and the other from the rear of the convoy, caught the jeeps and the Dodge under the crossfire of their bursts, killing three of the four drivers on the spot. Marcus's men, who were Moslems except for Company Sergeant-Major Bonnard and the drivers, jumped for the ditches, firing as they went. They were well trained, and they carried out this movement, which was their only possible course of action, at top speed. Now the fight was going to start: the company had brought along, mounted on the first jeep, a machine gun, with which they might be able to silence the enemy's two.

However, the only tommy-gun bursts and single rifle shots seemed to their trained ears to be coming from the roadside: there was no sound from their own machine gun. What was happening?

Marcus looked back at the jeep: the machine gun was not firing. The private who should have manned it, one of the Moslems, was crouching motionless in the bottom of the vehicle. Marcus began to crawl toward him. Before he had got halfway, the man suddenly jumped up beside his weapon. While the attackers' arms fell silent, he swiveled his mounting around and, at point-blank range, directed a stream of machine-gun fire on his comrades, who, with their backs turned to him, made a set of helpless sitting targets. It was calculated, unpardonable treachery.

Marcus, the man of the singlehanded show, the man whose war aim was love, foundering in this irreparable wreck of his hopes, deafened by the terrified screams of his men, who were being riddled in the back from the very direction where they expected support—Marcus leaped for the jeep, killed the traitor with his hands, and then swiveled the machine gun around again and started to fire. Of the twenty-three men in the convoy, only five were still able to fight—including himself. The rest were dead or wounded.

The invisible attackers, who had made the most of their cover, continued to sweep the road with their bursts of crossfire. There was no hope of getting out of it. Marcus's men were paralyzed by panic.

Marcus jumped into the midst of them, in the ditch. He shouted an order for his few men to follow him in an attack on one of the stolen machine guns.

Bousquine, who was pinned down on the ground with his legs smashed, saw two of the survivors refuse Marcus's orders and retreat along the ditch, throwing their arms away. The three others joined his attack, advancing in a series of rushes from bush to bush.

The sheet of fire continued uninterrupted. Bousquine, who had no desire to await the end of the story as a spectator, began to drag himself on his arms, lugging his useless legs behind him, looking for a hiding-place. He was a blood brother of the *fellagha*, and he knew how they would round the day off.

After a sudden crescendo of fire, which showed that Marcus and his commando were firing now, the din stopped. And then Bousquine, son of a penniless family of the Philippeville casbah, officer in the French army, persuaded by the man he adored, Major Marcus, to join him in the great gamble of real nomadization, cut off from his two brothers who had gone over to the *maquis*, sometimes racked by doubts, but at bottom certain he was serving a just cause in an honest experiment—Bousquine, terror-stricken and bleeding to death in a ditch, looked upon the final scene. A section of uniformed *fellagha* dashed down the slope onto the road, stripped his comrades of their arms and their clothes, cut out their eyes and everything else on their bodies that could be mutilated and then, on a whistle call from one of their number who had a red stripe or two on his shoulder, disappeared into the underbrush again.

Of Marcus there was not a sign. . . .

"The deserters from Marcus's own company were in the ambush," added Major Henry, precise and smart as always, winding up the story he had got from the survivors.

"How can you identify them?"

"They left one of the two machine guns behind them—the one Marcus attacked. He succeeded, too: the three *fellagha* who were manning the machine gun were killed, and the others hadn't the time to get away with it. That was one of the arms stolen from Marcus."

Bousquine was in his death throes. His eyes traveled slowly around the group of us. They seemed to express the same feeling that Bonnard had reported that morning when the arms were stolen: Bousquine was ashamed.

Espanieul moved close to him.

"We've got to go on," Bousquine said in a whisper in Espanieul's direction. "It's Kodja who did the killing. . . . I know it's him. . . . He wants to break everything off, everything . . . so that there's nothing left . . . hate . . . We've got to go on, tell Major Marcus."

Kodja was known in the rebellion as one of the leaders who have chosen the die-hard line, who want to fight on until the French are driven out.

They have deliberately gone in for extreme violence. In their scheme of things, brutality pays. It promotes among their troops the feeling of a holy and therefore a total war, and it provokes Frenchmen to a justifiable fury that, striking blindly, disgusts the Moslems not yet sure which side they are on. For these rebels, the worst crimes are the most effective. If they have to choose between liquidating a police officer who everyone knows is a monster and liquidating a Marcus who is trying to make contact, they will pick Marcus without a moment's hesitation. They want to do the most possible harm, to destroy any attempt at reconciliation or compromise. They must root out from Algerian soil, by terror if necessary, the slightest sentiment that might lead to a desire for an understanding. They are the "Stalinists" of the rebellion. They have staked their money on a complete smash-up.

On every level, from the Supreme Command of the National Liberation Front to its local officials (political commissioners, collectors of money, commanders of bands, and so forth), there are also men with a quite different outlook. They are known among the *fellagha* as "Bourguibists"—from Habib Bourguiba, the Arab statesman who is now President of Tunisia, and who led his country to independence without bloodshed. The "Bourguibists" fight alongside the "Stalinists" in the armed struggle, for their immediate objective is the same, an independent Algeria. But they disagree about everything else, and particularly about the nature of Algeria's future relations with France.

As the "Bourguibists" see it, any idea of driving the French out is madness, and when an Algerian state is finally founded, it will be done in agreement with France. Their view of how the guerrilla war and the terrorist campaign should be carried out is therefore quite different from that of the terrorists. Choosing between the detested police officer and Marcus, it is the policeman they set their killers on; Marcus they will try to contact. They are betting on the solution diametrically opposed to that of many of their associates; they are putting their money on a growth of understanding. They are against hatred. They are out for a short war, the others for a long one.

Throughout Algeria, as the war spreads, another test of strength is going on, a secret one within the revolt: Who is going to get command of it? Which doctrine will prevail? Is it better to press for a holy war or to be prepared for negotiations halfway?

The question is not settled yet. The faction fight among the rebel leaders has its ups and downs. Events and our own conduct sometimes favor one side, sometimes the other. Every time a Frenchman in a responsible position, civilian or military, controls his temper, insists on patience, and avoids punishing innocent people, he encourages a "Bourguibist" reaction among the Moslems. And in doing so he becomes a marked man for the "Stalinists," who, for their part, get the upper hand whenever the blindness of collective reprisals justifies their fanaticism.

The horrible butchery of Marcus's nomad company was an example that came after many others in our area, and it was going to be a test.

"We've got to go on," Bousquine had said before he died. Alas, it is so easy to think of self-control, so hard to practice it.

The other survivor of Marcus's convoy, the Moslem soldier who had escaped by a miracle and who was on the ground, bent and haggard, leaning against a tree—was he loyal or a traitor?

He was a comrade of the murdered victims, but he was also a comrade of the murderers, of the deserters and the traitor who had manned the convoy's machine gun. How should he be treated? As a friend to be protected from possible future vengeance, or as a potential traitor who might yield some useful information if he was "given the works"? Fundamentally, the "Stalinists," in Algeria and elsewhere, have everything in their favor: it is so much easier, on both sides, to be totalitarian, to respond with a total obedience to instinct, distrust, racialism.

Standing beside us was Captain Jouve, a tall, blond, athletic type, an officer of the Legion of Honor, President of the War Veterans' Association in a little town near Toulouse, who admired Marcus without understanding him ("a fellow like that," he would say, curving back the thumb of his right hand). He had collected his NCO's around him and was repeating the old, old advice in a picturesque re-edited form.

"This will be the last bloody mess, I hope. I'm getting fed up with being taken for a sucker. Here a great guy like Marcus treats them like pals, and that's how they say thanks. O.K., boys, we're wise to them. Now, you listen to me. Point one: on an operation, any gook who's walking more than three miles an hour, you fill him full of lead! Obviously he's only beating it. And that's that. Point two: if on an operation you see a gook standing still, you fire first; if he scrams, it shows he's got a guilty conscience. That's all. You get me?"

A roar of laughter greeted his words. An enormous desire to let go, after the unbearable sight of the massacre's aftermath, gave free rein to the deep-seated feeling that demands vengeance. And the most satisfying vengeance is the simplest and the most brutal—physical vengeance.

"Jouve," Espanieul cut him short, "I am giving orders here. You and these other officers will follow me to the Louvois post. I will give you my instructions."

Espanieul knew only too well what might happen: the outburst after an ambush, the sacking of the neighboring *mechtas*, which are treated as if they were all accomplices of the attackers. He did not have a very high opinion of Marcus and his experiment ("too sentimental, all that"), but he was also fully aware that blind reprisals are, from any point of view, the very best way of helping the enemy. On the way to Louvois, where we were to spend the night, he discussed with Henry the best way of dispatching on Marcus's trail, not a pack of men under the influence of a Jouve, but—if possible—a body of soldiers.

5/ The sentry at the entrance to the Louvois post examined the occupants of the three jeeps in the glare of his flashlight, then pulled back the roll of barbed wire that blocked the way and let us in.

All was silence.

Espanieul, who generally felt in top form at midnight, jumped out first and shouted to the man on guard to get the OC of the post.

We were in the sandy little central parade ground, surrounded by tents. In the middle was a flagpole, from which the colors floated from six in the morning to six at night.

A light went on in one of the tents. On its canvas wall we had a shadow-show view of the hurried gestures of a silhouette tucking a shirt into a hastily pulled-on pair of trousers. The next moment a round figure in a delightful state of disarray emerged on the double and presented itself.

"Second Lieutenant Bodard, OC Louvois post. Good evening, sir."

The words, pronounced in a warm southern accent, were military; the appearance was less so.

Bodard was a likable reservist of twenty-six, a former student of the School of Arts and Crafts. He was a conscientious and indeed a courageous fellow, but he bemoaned every day—he made no secret of it—his drawing-board in a big chemical works in the Pyrenees. He had not yet succeeded in understanding the necessity of his exile to a peak in the south of Algeria.

"Bodard," said Espanieul, "get your men together. I want to talk to them."

"But—they're all asleep, sir." Bodard had assumed the startled, almost indignant air of a nurse protecting her children.

"Good," said Espanieul in a surprisingly calm voice. "I'll explain in a moment what it's all about. If I tell you to wake your men, it's because I need them. See that they're roused, and come with us to your tent: we've got an operation to work out."

The afternoon's events were explained to Bodard, and then Espanieul outlined for us the plan Henry and he had thought out. The first consideration was to avoid, as far as possible, letting loose on the countryside a large and vengeful body of troops who would empty the area of its last inhabitants. The second was to try not to frighten the *fellagha* band, which would avoid battle and vanish into thin air if our strength was, as was usually the case, too overwhelming. The answer was to set out in search of Marcus in two light columns of ten men, without ostensible support. These patrols would naturally remain in radio contact with the main body of the troops in the rear.

Tackled in this way, however, the job was a dangerous one, and Espanieul wanted only volunteers for it.

"Oh, in that case . . . Volunteers . . . You won't get them," Bodard said at once, with a quiet assurance.

Henry, the former cadet of Saint-Cyr and hero of Indochina, turned his carefully combed blond head toward Bodard with a disdainful expression.

"If what you say is right, Bodard, and out of the fifty reservists under your orders here there isn't a single volunteer, allow me to tell you that you are responsible. It means you haven't got a grip on your men, you've got no authority over them."

Bodard was a civilian to the core. He had told himself from the start that the game would be over in six months at the outside and that it was just a rough time to get through. Saint-Cyrians did not impress him: he didn't give a damn what they might think. The letter he had received this week from his boss was very nice. He had done three and a half months of service already; in less time than that he would be demobbed. So why should he be a sucker tonight, even if it was midnight and the *fellagha* had behaved like bastards?

"Oh," he said with an expressive grimace, "you'll get two or three hotheads, all right—chaps who get a kick out of it—but not the others. Can't expect them to overdo it. If you give them an order, they'll obey: it isn't that they're chicken. No. But when it comes to volunteering, you mustn't count on them. No . . ."

The colonel shrugged his shoulders and went out.

In the central square, around the flagpole, the fifty men of the post were lined up in three groups. They had dressed in a hurry: two or three still wore pajama tops, and several were in slippers.

Standing in the entrance of the tent, we looked on at the scene: Espanieul, with his back to us, was talking to these boyish young men whose faces we could not distinguish. Then he came back to us.

"I called for ten volunteers. Not at once: five minutes to think it over. And those who decide to volunteer are to come and see us in the tent. I got a good impression—they're a nice-looking bunch. All we have to do is to wait. . . . I'd feel pretty sick, all the same, if I had to order men to do this job."

Bodard had returned to his men: he identified with them, never exercising the authority his stripes gave him without a certain sense of discomfort. He generally tried to persuade them "as one pal to another" before he resigned himself to giving an order.

His comrades, who had been nonplussed by the colonel's little pep talk, had stayed where they were, hardly breaking ranks: one or two were discussing the venture, but most of them were silent.

In the tent, over little bottles of far-too-warm beer—the truck that brought a little ice to the posts had not come that week—we marveled, from the depths of our tiredness, that Espanieul was still so wide awake. Even Julienne, who had an iron constitution, was almost done in by the long day's work.

Bodard came back, with an apathetic but obedient air— the perfect complement to his accent. With the mien of one who is saying "I told you so," he approached the colonel:

"There are one or two, always the same ones. . . . Would you like to see them?"

"Of course. Have them come in, one at a time."

A dumpy little man entered, extraordinarily broad in the body for his height, with a handsome face burned dark by the sun, black crinkly hair, and a straight nose. He wore a shirt open at the neck. His chin was pulled in and his neck was held very straight. He stood at attention.

"Corporal Lapierre, Second Company, Third Section."

"You're volunteering?"

"Yes, sir."

"Fine!" And, turning to us: "Good-looking fellow, isn't he? . . . D'you mind my asking you why?" he said to the corporal.

"I'm always game when it comes to showing the gooks that we're not soft. . . . And then we haven't got a goddam thing to do around here. It's two months now since I came up here, and it's enough to brown anyone off. The rest of the guys, they're just waiting to be demobbed, but I'd rather have a job to do."

"Excellent. Get into battle dress, then, and wait outside. You'll get your instructions in a moment."

With a final irreproachable salute, Lapierre went out, obviously delighted to be in the limelight.

"Well, he's not so bad, is he? He's an eager beaver, no doubt about that," said Espanieul, who was not sorry to be able to show once more what he could do with men. Looking at Bodard, he asked: "Has he got influence over the others? What does he do in civil life?"

Shrugging his plump shoulders, Bodard, who seemed much less enthusiastic than the colonel, put things in their proper perspective.

"I told you there were one or two who have a screw loose," he said. "That guy, and there's another like him—they're both Commies. They're the ones we had all the trouble with in France before we left. Mutinies, sabotage, scrawling on the walls about the 'filthy war'—they were agitators, no doubt about it. They handed out Party leaflets to their buddies in camp, and even at Marseilles. Since they've been here—well, that's another story. By the end of a month they were the biggest flag-wavers of the whole bunch. They want to be tough guys. In France they showed the others how big they were by stirring up trouble against the officers; here they want to hunt gooks. . . . It's the same thing."

Bodard's little lecture on the local volunteer was no surprise to us now; we had heard it all before and had ceased to be astonished. Twenty or so reputed Communists had attracted the attention of Military Security at the assembly camp in France by their activities. They showed a hell of a lot of nerve, even going so far as to stir up full-scale riots against parachutist officers. But, once they were on Algerian soil, most of them had become the most resolute of all the *fellagha*-hunters.

The transformation was curious to watch. As the days passed and the separation from their normal motor center grew longer, some of these boys, whose energy was obvious, began to waver; they no longer knew where to direct their enthusiasm, or how. They began to be confused. They drifted. Then little by little their energy and their smart talk returned. They discovered a new direction for their overwhelming compulsion to distinguish themselves: all they needed was to be even more military than the others, always on tap when it came to "maintaining order," more certain than anyone else of their superiority to the "little rats." After a period of distrust, the officers of the regiment got used to this change of skin and ended up by regarding these Commies-turned-patriots as their most dependable men. They were not only good at working over suspects, but they also knew how to keep their own comrades quiet, if the occasion arose. The other Communists, the ones who would never change, had been sent elsewhere.

"Good, that makes two already. Got to take what you can get. After all, if you could turn all the Communists into workers for pacification, it wouldn't be so bad. Just look at them, they're certainly guys we can use. Well, what's next?"

Bodard called in a thin, muscular boy of about thirty. He had a small, well-trimmed, blond mustache, and a lofty expression gave his hollow-cheeked face some character.

"Sergeant Brique, Second Company, First Section. At your service, sir."

There was no need for explanation about this man. Brique was an old acquaintance of mine. As he talked to the colonel, it occurred to me that he was a symbol of my war in Algeria. He had represented a difficult moment for me.

It had happened three weeks after we arrived. My presence in the regiment had been commented on, and I knew that one little group of NCO's in particular were more than reserved about it; they were determined not to make my job an easy one. Three veterans of the Colonial Army who had been in Indochina stood out in this group. One of them was Sergeant Brique.

Brique and his friends were not in my company, and I had no contact with them. But one day I received orders to take into my company a section of those curious and seemingly outmoded machines called half-tracks. Following normal procedure, I sent for the second lieutenant in charge of the machines and told him to assemble his section at full strength next morning, when I would inspect it before taking command.

The section, correctly dressed, duly paraded and then divided into little groups commanded by sergeants. I asked the second lieutenant to introduce the sergeant of each as I went down the line.

First group: Sergeant Boumier. Good morning. Good morning, sir, etc.

Second group: Sergeant Brique. Absent, on sick call.

Third group: Sergeant Channin. Good morning . . .

Fourth group: Sergeant Valaud. Absent, on sick call.

What? Two sergeants on sick call? Funny . . .

"Send them to headquarters tomorrow so that I can meet them."

Next day, right on time, there was Brique, standing at attention.

"Sergeant Brique, sir. You sent for me?"

"Yes, Brique . . . Is anything wrong, aren't you well?"

Brique's face, set and inscrutable, his eyes fixed on the horizon, did not flinch. There was no reply.

"I want to know why you were on sick call yesterday when I made the inspection."

There was no reply.

"Come on, Brique, cut the comedy. Let's get it straight: if you have something to say to me, say it. If not, you'll be put on report, and that's that."

"Well, sir, me and Valaud, we're good Frenchmen!"

Now we were getting somewhere.

"Well?"

"Well . . . It's difficult to tell you. It's your political opinions. You see, we're *good Frenchmen!*"

The man was obviously lit, as well. To steel himself for this conversation, he had apparently sought Dutch courage from an early-morning glass of straight brandy, which, as a matter of fact, he was holding very well.

I had to find some way out. I could not involve myself in a political discussion. It was not my business either to listen to him or to preach at him; we were not here for that. But to let him go on repeating to me *ad nauseam* that he was a *good Frenchman* was impossible. We would end up slugging it out, and, as I was an officer, I would obviously be in the wrong. That was exactly what he and his friends wanted.

The silence had already lasted too long.

"Listen to me, Brique. . . . Your political opinions don't concern me. I don't want to know anything about them. If you're a good Frenchman, you've got a duty here: to obey orders. When you're back in civilian life, you can do what you like, and possibly we can resume this conversation. At the moment, you're under my orders, and you will report to me according to regulations. Tomorrow morning at eight o'clock I shall make another inspection of the section, and I shall expect Valaud and you to be there."

He left.

Next morning I got a tip-off. Brique would be at the inspection, but he intended, in front of everyone, to refuse to salute me when I passed in front of him.

This was the knock-out round. If I let Brique get away with refusing to salute me and pretended not to notice it, I was sunk. If, on the other hand, I called him on it, with all the men watching, there would be an incident. The men would certainly have more sympathy for him than for me. He lived with them. I had known them only twenty-four hours. Yet it was equally impossible to backtrack and call off the inspection. This trifling incident had become a test.

At eight o'clock I began my inspection of the section with the group on the left. Brique's was the next.

In my recognition of the implications of the affair and in my fear of the moment of truth, I had forgotten one thing: Brique was in the same fix as I was. For him, too, it was a test. I might be in the bull ring with all the gates shut, but he was there, too. If he went through with his plan, if at the last moment he stuck to his guns and actually refused to salute me, was it so certain that he would have the last word? Or even that the crowd would be with him? Reservists couldn't always be counted on, far from it: if he were the first to make trouble, he would be a marked man.

Everything went off in a flash, as always happens with the things that matter. An exchange of looks, or the electricity in the air, or the fact that one actor is perhaps more tired than the other, or that someone's nerves are more frayed because of a drink he has had earlier—heaven knows what one condition among hundreds of unknown, uncontrollable factors suddenly determines the act itself. Brique's eyes were still lost in the distance, his fingers were trembling from being held taut, but, after an interminable hesitation of one or two seconds, he—and I don't know why to this day—brought his hand to his cap. . . .

"Very good, Brique, thank you," said Espanieul, to end their talk. "We know we can always count on you. Do you think that many of your buddies will volunteer?"

"I don't think so, sir. They're chicken."

"Chicken! Well, I'll be damned. About what? Getting into a scrap?" Espanieul, veteran of the Leclerc column, sixteen times mentioned in dispatches, was thunderstruck. But he was on the wrong track.

"No, sir," Bodard put in calmly. "It's not the scrap, it's the volunteering. If you order them to go, they'll go and they'll do a damn good job. But you won't get anywhere by asking them to volunteer. Even if some of them wanted to, they wouldn't dare admit it in front of their buddies. They're not chicken—they're *ashamed* of volunteering. Don't hold it against them—it's natural. . . ."

"But, really," said Espanieul, "I can't believe it. You aren't going to tell me that the only volunteers in your company are Communists and Fascists? I can't believe it!"

Henry knew more about the troops' morale than Espanieul. When he had told Bodard: "If you don't get volunteers, you're to blame," he was right, in a sense. He knew that in some sections, every time volunteers were called for, *everyone* stepped forward, and in others *no one* did. It depended on the personality of the officer or NCO in command of the section: whether he had a grip on the men or not. But whether everyone volunteered or no one, it boiled down to the same thing: none of the men wanted to single himself out from the others. Bodard had been right: they were not cowards—in fact, most of them were very steady under fire. But to *volunteer* to do more than the others, to take on extra duty when it was not required—that, they felt with muddle-headed certainty, would be subscribing to the whole business. It would be as though they approved of being drafted. They would, in fact, become active participants, no longer just submissive and neutral objects. . . . No. Their officers might give them whatever orders they felt like; it wasn't the men's business to argue. But no one must ask them their opinion.

Espanieul had to face the facts: as volunteers there were only the two ex-Communists and Sergeant Brique.

Outside the tent where we were gathered, a quiet hum of conversation showed that the men were talking it over. In the distance, isolated shots and abrupt bursts of fire were answering one another. We had almost forgotten that what we were up to was not an interesting evening of inquiry into the nature of the mid-twentieth-century man, and that instead we were concerned with the urgent preparation of an operation whose object was to find Marcus.

A young sergeant entered the tent. We knew him: it was Baral, nicknamed Bunny, a small, dark, intelligent man. He held sway over many of his comrades through a more than average ability to put his thoughts into words. A couple of timid privates accompanied him, one on either side: it was a real delegation.

Espanieul was fond of Baral: in the beginning he had taken him on as his orderly. But Baral, bored by the job, had asked to go back to the others in his unit.

"Well, Bunny, I expect you're a volunteer, aren't you?"

"That's what I've come to see you for, sir. It seems you told Sergeant Brique to tell us we were a bunch of sissies. So we've come to explain what it's all about. If you want us all to go on the patrol tonight, the boys'll all go. We're not afraid, but you've got to give us orders. Volunteering—no, the boys won't do it."

"And why not? You make me sick. What are you afraid of? I'll tell you: you're afraid of being called suckers by two or three agitators among you. That's what it boils down to."

"No, sir, it's not only that. It's true there are some who don't want it to be said when they get back to their jobs in France that they've been volunteers. Take Truffié, of Renault's—he says that if he was to volunteer, they'd knock his block off when he got back. Maybe there are a dozen like him; it's a question of trade unions. But there are others who haven't got a reason like that. They don't like being here, that's all. They're not *against*, but they feel they're not being treated right. You know, the chow's not so great, and they've promised us barracks for two months and they still haven't come, and we often do three hours of guard duty a night and more until we're beat. The guys just don't like it. They're browned off."

One of the privates standing a little behind Baral started to think aloud, and then began to talk more clearly:

"That's not all. Look at how they've bitched up our families. The boys get letters from home, their wives are asking for money, but we haven't drawn a penny of our pay yet. It's been going on for months. We've got nothing to send home, and there's nobody there to pull in a paycheck in our place. At first when we got letters like that we told them not to worry: they'd be sure to get something, either from the army or from the works. But after three letters, what do you expect us to tell them? Well, we just stop writing. But we think about it all the time, and it's not good for morale."

Espanieul listened with rapt attention. He was discovering the distance which, though he had never realized it before, separated his vision of France at war from the realistic picture drawn by this regiment in the field. The distance was too great. The hero of the Fezzan emerged sorrowfully from his golden dream.

Smoothing back his thick black hair with a tired hand and keeping his other hand in the rear pocket of his parachutist's uniform, he stared at Baral.

"Baral . . . France—doesn't that mean anything to your little buddies?"

The young sergeant wavered in the face of so incongruous a question. He pulled a little pipe out of his jacket and began to play with it, as if contact with this familiar object would reassure him of the reality of things.

"I really don't understand what you mean to say, sir—or, rather, I don't see the connection. But I can see you don't think much of us, and there I think you're wrong.

Here's what my buddies told me to tell you: if you give us the order to go, we'll go—no one's got the jitters. But don't count on them to volunteer."

The curious delegation withdrew.

The question was settled: Bodard, on the colonel's orders, was to pick seven men who, with the three "patriots," would accompany us in two light patrols in pursuit of the band.

It was nearly two in the morning. We had taken off at five. There was not much time for rest.

The hum of talk outside, which had grown quieter, stopped as soon as Bodard had picked the men: everyone except the men on guard duty had gone back to bed. We were impatiently waiting to follow suit. Espanieul, however, was apparently deaf to our pleas. He was pacing up and down the tent with his hands thrust firmly in his revolver pockets, his head bent forward. He could not bring himself to leave it at that.

His green eyes, which had become almost childlike in face of the unknown, turned on Julienne. "You, now, what what do *you* say to that? Does it seem normal to you?"

Julienne was exhausted. But Espanieul was not a man to be brushed aside. An opportunity of probing the nature of things with him, if only for a few minutes, was worth taking. Raising his big round head with its clipped gray hair, and wrinkling his brow so as to see Espanieul better, Julienne began to talk with a brusque intensity.

"Frankly . . . yes. I should say it's your astonishment that surprises me, not their attitude. Look at their position. They've lived only within their own country. They've never had questions. Here they are for the first time outside: they're looking at France from the outside. You see what I'm getting at. It's rather as if a bunch of kids had been taken as adults from their mothers' womb and were looking at her for the first time—a mother whom they'd never seen before, never even pictured. What does it look like to them? Let's be honest. Their picture of France isn't a collection of colored postcards; their view is the life they lead here. First, it's all loused up—no huts, money not coming in, and the rest of it. Then there's this curious 'protection' of Algeria, the gooks, who make them sick and whom they kill like rabbits, and the Frenchman here, who've treated them like mud. What else? What meaning is there, what purpose—what possible reason for giving up two hours of sleep?"

"You might as well be saying that France doesn't exist!"

"No, I'm saying that, in concrete terms, France is the face she shows us, seen from the outside—seen from here. You see it as I do. But their picture of France leaves them cold at best, and they try not to think about it any more. It's the same with almost all of them. Naturally, they're obsessed with material difficulties, because they have nothing better to think about."

Julienne rose from his chair and went over to Espanieul, as if he wanted to speak more softly.

"And then there are the others—the ones who want to give themselves up to something, to throw themselves headlong into a big adventure. Do you know what becomes of that kind? They become Cadet Maillots,[2] or else instruments of justice in the counter-terrorist torture chamber—and it amounts to the same thing. Those are the boys who can't bear living in a void when they have a need, a physical need, for passion. Like the others, they are looking for the Fatherland, the country that has armed them. But they see this blurred, disorderly, unrecognizable picture—this nothing-

[2] French army cadet, a member of the Communist Party, who went over to the *fellagha* with the arms of his section.

ness. Well, they've got to throw themselves into something, it doesn't matter what. They become either killers or traitors. And we're the ones who are responsible."

"We? It's the regime that stinks. A regime that can send us out young men like that . . . It's unbelievable!"

"Remember, sir, that when you were with Leclerc, coming up from Chad, these boys weren't ten years old. You carry about with you the living image of a great adventure, and you relive it every day: it burns up the trash of everyday mediocrity. What interior fire have they been given? In the name of what are they to stand up to their difficulties? What are they to think of when they clench their teeth?"

Slowly, as if every movement were painful, Espanieul took his hands out of his pockets and went out of the tent.

The rest of us stood up. In less than two hours we would have to start. The hurricane lamps were extinguished.

As he went out, Major Henry, who had a more clear-cut diagnosis, repeated to Julienne a typical army phrase, one that particularly pleased him:

"It adds up to this, the reservists are full of shit."

Julienne did not bother to answer. The arguments he was turning in his mind were too arduous for him to make the effort.

No, to be sure—the reservists are France itself.

6/ The two patrols left Louvois before dawn, so that each would be able to cover a wide area carefully and methodically. Henry was in command of one, Julienne of the other. The rest of the troops remained in reserve, ready if they were called on. The patrols kept radio contact with Espanieul's headquarters, at the roadside where the ambush had taken place.

I was with Henry. The day was long and monotonous.

The countryside was almost deserted. As always, terror had drawn off all signs of life; everyone who could move had fled. The *fellagha's* brutal threats to make an example by immediate and savage execution of anyone reporting on their movements had had the customary effect. And the firing of our tank patrols (the kind of firing which is now called in the official jargon *"a priori,"* meaning that you fire before you know what you are firing at) had done its work also.

The only people we saw were a few women and old men squatting like inanimate objects in scraps of gardens in front of abandoned houses.

We made no attempt to hide ourselves. On the contrary, the purpose of these light patrols was to act as a sort of bait and through our relative weakness draw the enemy band into an engagement. We only hoped that the lookouts would do their job and report that we were there.

It was getting late. We had barely time to get back to base before nightfall.

The march back was tougher than all the rest of the day put together. Our feet were hurting us, we had seen nothing that gave us a clue to the whereabouts of Marcus, and with the close of day the villages took on the appearance of effigies in a waxworks—the same old men and the same women were squatting in the same abandoned places.

The journey seemed endless. Our volunteers were converting their disappointment into angry aggression—but they had nothing to kill. The others, who didn't care, started to ask Henry whether they were going to get some chow on the way, or whether they would have to wait till they got back to the post. Henry was in good condition and stood up to the strain despite an old wound at the back of the neck which was hurting him (he had had to hand his rifle to Bunny). But he was afraid that Julienne's patrol might have run into something and had a rough time of it.

As we neared the road we began to hear the rumbling of the armored patrols at regular intervals.

Just about this time last night we had heard of the sudden tragedy that had knocked out Marcus's convoy. One more drama on top of so many others—already we had the feeling that we were doing just a routine job.

At the temporary camp they were waiting for the return of our patrol; we had told them over our portable radio that we were en route. Julienne and his crew were not back yet. But they had made radio contact, too, and their last message reported that they had found Marcus—dead, with his three last *goumiers*. Julienne, carrying in a sack the body of his friend, horribly mutilated with an ax, was on the way back.

In one of the gutted houses that abutted the road at the tactical headquarters, Espanieul was in conference. He was with another officer whom we knew well but had rarely had the opportunity of seeing in our sector. It was Colonel Galland, the man responsible for co-ordination between the eastern and western areas of the operational sectors.

As usual, a multitude of little details indicated the presence of Galland: the way people behaved and spoke, the way the vehicles were parked, the way the empty ration cans were disposed of—it was never quite the same when you knew Galland was there. Lieutenant Martin, who had served under him in the Laos *maquis*, and Espanieul, who had followed him across Libya in the campaign against Rommel, spoke of Galland in the same words, with the same intonation and the same puckering of the eyes and the lips: "There's a soldier for you!"

Which meant, among other things, that Colonel Galland had no friends: real command implies solitude. It meant that, though he was married and had five children, he had moved thirty times in twenty years so as to be always on the battlefield, wherever the French army, no matter what the job, was to be found. It meant that, because he had come to hate the way lies and bluff had debased military life as it had the nation, he had made it a hard and fast rule never to read anything into events or even to guess; rather, he would stick to hard facts and with all his power set himself against trifling with accuracy. It meant that, though he had been a colonel for nearly ten years and had covered himself with glory and with wounds, he was still not a general, a scandal that was due to his obstinate refusal to drop into Ministers' offices to "have a chat." . . . Yes, Galland was a soldier, all right: there are a few of them still left.

In a corner of the roofless house, sitting on a case of K-rations, tracing idle figures in the yellow dust with the branch he held in his hand, Galland was listening to Espanieul. The latter was pacing from one wall to the other in jerky strides, telling him about the night at the post and the way our men were feeling.

The news of Marcus's death helped to throw the latest episodes into a peculiar relief. In fact, nothing had occurred that was very different from what had been going on every week for three months. All the same, the feeling that something had to be done was overwhelming. Espanieul, too, felt what Julienne and Marcus had been discussing together. Martin, Henry—all in their own ways, and for different reasons, were becoming conscious of the need for action.

Galland had trained himself to mental discipline. He listened gravely as Espanieul finished his long story:

"What worries me the most, and what makes me sick, is this inconsistency. Mind you, I've no time for the sniveling of worthy Christian souls about the 'poor Moslems' who are so maltreated. That's beside the point. The worst political mistake is to mix up collective morals with individual morals." Since Espanieul had read *The Taxis of the Marne* he never passed up an opportunity to quote this brisk formula. "But that's not knowing what you want. If they were to tell us: go on killing Arabs till they keep quiet—as the Americans did with the Red Indians—I wouldn't be against it *a priori*. Technically, it would make sense. But, officially, it isn't what they want. What is it, then? You've got to admit that these reservists, for all their stupidity, aren't altogether wrong: what are they being asked to do?"

"Listen, Espanieul," Galland began, "let's take things in order. . . ."

Having indicated that he was going to talk, Galland let the silence give him another moment for reflection.

"There are the things that are most urgent and the things that are most serious: they aren't necessarily the same. The most serious is the young people. The most urgent is the army. Every day I tell myself that the moral bankruptcy of our young men, which is shocking enough when they arrive, may well be irreparable after their experience here. That is, unless we find a way of harnessing them to a job that has some meaning. It's not easy—but it could be done. We'll talk about that another time. The most urgent job is else-where: the fate of the army is in the balance. Through certain of its elements—unfortunately, the most conspicuous, which means that all the others are marked—the army has even become here and there an active instrument of counter-terrorism. In one or two places in these sectors, punitive expeditions have been launched by the more hotheaded of the local Frenchmen. I can understand their edginess, but that they should do this with the complicity of the army—that's not to be tolerated."

Galland stood up. He continued to draw little lines on the earth of one of the walls that was still standing.

"This morning I saw the mayor of the village of Ridj. He told me: 'I can't be responsible for the upkeep of the roads any more.' What upkeep? 'Picking up the corpses.' In his commune it sometimes happens that they find between six and ten Moslem corpses dumped in the ditches—and that's not counting the ones which are hidden. He knows very well which of his friends go in for these nighttime jobs, and up to now he's avoided this delicate subject. But now they've got us in a corner: everyone knows that our vehicles are used to settle some accounts. The way he tried to let me know it—'Since your men are in on the job, you might as well take charge of removing the rubbish too'—made me want to strangle him on the spot. But what was I to do? I couldn't answer him. So look out: this is the really urgent business. The army is the only thing we've got left that's clean. There would be nothing left to cling to."

Listening to Galland, we experienced a reaction of sanity brought about by his statement of forgotten truths. In this senseless war, it was a rare and priceless pleasure. Those who, like Galland, preserved in their souls the simple rules of honor and of justice were a small elite, and almost all of them were Gaullists of 1940.

When you have grown accustomed to watching and listening to the men who bear the same label in political life, it is difficult to imagine the character of the "Gaullists" in the other world that the army represents. In the army world they are almost all replicas of the Commander. They would not accept the things that go on which most of the other army types condone—at least by shutting their eyes. They remain as vigilant as if they were De Gaulle himself. And in a way they are. Within themselves they preserve the exacting vision of France which they one day built up in exile.

Galland was a constant example of the true Gaullist. For us he embodied a hope, an opportunity to act again.

Julienne had now joined the large group surrounding Galland. Right away he showed that he wanted to listen to Galland, to discuss with us the grave problems that Marcus had faced up to—and not the condition of Marcus's corpse.

After the long days of bitterness, uncertainty, inconsistency, and sometimes shame, all the men who were gathered here—the resigned and the rebellious, the conservatives and the liberals, the veterans of Free France and the young men of the France of today—felt that the night was falling not only on the ruins that surrounded us, but on a period of our service in Algeria, a period that was now over. It was inconceivable that the future, too, should turn into the same monotonous absurdity. From where we stood in the great venture, something new would surely be tried.

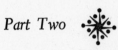

Part Two

The Hope

Chapter One

The hundred or so men, ranged in little troops of five, presented an unusual spectacle. Each wore a black knitted Arab cap and, around the waist, a broad band of black flannel. Each had a sort of light knapsack hanging from his belt. They looked exactly like a band of *fellagha*. The only indication that the men were our own *maquisards* was that every fifth man carried a square box with a projecting wire which looked suspiciously like a radio set. And this little group gathered there, representing barely the strength of a company—this black pinhead in the huge army of Algeria embodied all our hopes. Or perhaps our illusions.

After two days of rest, the "Black Commandos" were going back on their fifth "nomadization" campaign among the Arabs.

Colonel Galland, like Marcus before him, had pinpointed the essential objective: to re-establish contact with the Moslem population. Everything else depended on that.

I still have the text of a memorandum that Galland and Espanieul drew up between them and sent to the Army Command. It described the blind alley into which the routine of the war was leading us, and the nature of the military problem.

. . . *Officers who took part in a few campaigns in Indochina have been startled to find that the position of the army (in its relations with the native population) is worse than it ever was in Vietnam. We are not speaking, of course, of the comparative strength of the opposing military forces, but of contacts and collaboration with the local populace. The ability of the people of Indochina to provide information and to defend them-*

selves remained satisfactory to the end, and bears no relation to the vacuum with which the military authorities find themselves faced here. . . .

There is, therefore, a danger that the Algerian rebellion may not need nearly so much military strength as did the Vietminh army to put the French army in a difficult position. . . . If that unfortunate day were to arrive, it would mean not only that the policy in the name of which the army was sent here had failed, but also that the responsibility for the failure would be placed once again on the army itself. At all costs, we must prevent things from coming to that pass. . . .

The key to the situation can be found in one very definite point: contact with the Moslem population. Contact today is almost nonexistent: it has been constantly shrinking. How is such contact to be revived? . . .

Throughout the army of Africa, probably a couple of hundred or more reports such as this have been drawn up, as clear as they are convincing. And they always end with the same conclusion: we must, at all costs, resume contact with the people and regain their confidence, or the game is up. These ideas are not new, either in Algeria or anywhere else. They were not new even in Vercingetorix's day. But how are they to be translated into action? How is one to draw up in concrete form a plan of local action—as Marcus had wanted it—and how does one show that it will work? For, of course, only the attempt counts, not the diagnosis.

Since that day on the Sakamody road when Galland, by speaking his mind, had stimulated our thinking, which had been so vague and so negative, a taste for action had become stronger than discouragement. The pilot experiment of the Black Commandos had been born.

In the beginning, Espanieul was the most fervent. He

was certain that, little by little, we could embrace the whole army of Africa and change the very nature of the Algerian situation. He was more than a propagandist, he was a crusader. And there was no one of any importance, either at Headquarters or at the Government-General, on whom he had not called to plead his case. Twice he had seen the Minister Resident himself.

Galland, though just as enthusiastic, was more reserved. He was far more familiar than Espanieul with the venomous hostility that the army brass will spew at any idea which threatens to disturb the foundations of their power. Imagine asking generals to chop up their magnificently organized, armored, powerful units, which were to them objects of such pride and, above all, signs of importance, into so many slices of salami and scatter them about the countryside. It was pure insanity. But, faced with the results of the normal methods of "pacification," Galland had found the energy to set his shoulder to the wheel.

Henry was enthusiastic enough. He had brought back from his campaigns in Indochina colorful and stirring memories of the *maquis* he had organized in the heart of the jungle in the Thai country. Almost every night, in the old garage, he would tell us one of his dozens of treasured stories about his exploits. We could see how the bitterness of France's defeat had almost wiped out his awareness of her influence on these strange and sensitive people. Henry was still in love with the Indochinese; he dreamed of going back there and living among them for the rest of his days. He felt no sort of attraction for the Arabs, but the adventure in itself appealed to him. The Black Commandos could be his corner of poetry in a dark and disillusioning war.

Even Martin was shaken. In spite of his respect for military regulations and his oversimplified definition of anti-Communism which had given him such a black-and-white view of the situation ("the *fellagha* are Viets"), his practical intelligence had never stopped working. The vacuum in which this huge army was operating, the ineffectiveness of so many efforts—all this had led Martin to search for "something new." What, it was difficult to say. The ground was already dangerously crumbling. Martin, as resourceful as he was self-assured, did not like to take his ideas from others: with this reservation, he too saw in the Black Commandos a chance of getting out of the soup.

Each, according to his own viewpoint, had found in the idea a way of not giving up. Gambert, the "Volunteer of the French Union," thought that "it was exactly the idea that Biaggi had tried to carry out." Julienne had lost faith in pacification. But he had stayed on to contribute his share toward making something better than racialists and potential assassins out of all these young men. He had thrown himself wholeheartedly into the commando squads. He was always out in the countryside now and had sacrificed his captain's insignia to command one of our little flying squads.

The text of the pledge which the volunteers for these commandos took, and which was published in the Algiers papers, defined the spirit of the venture. Here it is:

> I agree to serve in a squad of the new nomad commandos, whose mission is to restore a feeling of confidence to the Algerian people and to make conditions unsafe for the fellagha.
>
> I know that these light squads will have to live on their own and, should the occasion arise, defend themselves unaided for several days and nights running. They will often have to go through difficult country. I understand the risks, and I accept them.
>
> I also promise on my honor to observe the rule of the new nomad commandos: I will regard every Moslem

*as a friend and not as a suspect, unless I have proof to
the contrary.*

*I understand the additional risks I shall run as a
result of this rule. They are indispensable to the success
of our mission, and I freely accept them.*

The experiment of the Black Commandos was a limited
one. In terms of space, it covered only a small corner of one
of the many operational sectors of Algeria. In terms of time,
it began by using reservists who had only two or three more
months to serve before they were relieved.

But it had been quick to attract attention. The General
Staff, like the Algiers newspapers, had realized that the implications of the experiment far outran its immediate scale; it
was a question of a new trend, of an attitude of mind con-
fronting the realities of Algeria, of a new way of handling
the problem. If the germ of an idea that these little commandos contained were to develop and other experiments on
similar lines were to be tried throughout the army of Africa,
it might be necessary to recast completely the existing
methods of pacification. The experiment was followed with
rapt attention, friendly and otherwise.

Galland was aware of this. Despite other responsibilities
he encountered at his headquarters—some far away from our
area of action—he never failed to be on the spot when one
of our nomadization campaigns began.

His careful movements, his lined features, his spotless
battle-dress jacket, the left sleeve of which was sewed up
under the shoulder because of the arm he had lost in Indochina, the obvious control he exercised all the time over
his actions and his words—everything about him showed
his contempt for anything that was too easy, done without
effort. This distinctive manner helped him as a commander;
it compelled attention.

He was just ending a talk to the squad commanders, who were assembled in the briefing-room—a onetime class-room.

"Gentlemen, it depends on you whether the technique of these nomad commandos will be adopted on a big scale. The Commander-in-Chief and the Minister Resident have made special visits here. Your successes and your failures are noted, studied, and recorded. If through your efforts and your behavior you succeed in winning the respect of the Mos-lems, you may make a big change in their state of mind in this area. Your task is the most difficult which could be entrusted to a unit in Algeria—as you have already realized. . . . One last word: be careful. The very nature of your work demands that you should not be the first to fire—that you start by trusting people, which means the maximum of risk. That's agreed. Don't go any further. Be on your toes the whole time—all the more, I might add, since your atti-tude and your behavior can't reveal this. Don't get your-selves killed stupidly by mistaking coolness for carelessness: you would be doing serious harm to the reputation of these squads. Thank you. Good luck!"

The little room, warm from the gathering of so many men, began to buzz with talk. Before they left to assemble their men, each squad commander was asking for the things he needed: a map of the area he was going through, a rocket to summon help, money for meals, first-aid equipment. . . . But the briefing was not yet over. When Galland had fin-ished, Henry stood up and called for silence.

"You're going to be split up into ten areas, two teams to each, which cover the entire Jebel Kerrouch district. In this district there are about a dozen incidents a week—telephone lines cut, crops burned, sabotages, and crimes of violence. Not one has been reported to us by the populace; some of the incidents we discovered only two or three days later. Obviously, the rebels are being screened by the inhabitants of the *mechtas* that extend from the Jebel Kerrouch to the Wadi Ahmar. Your business will be to get among these people, thaw them out, discover the immediate reasons for this new crop of incidents and, if possible, isolate those responsible. A word of warning: don't sleep in the *mechtas* after the evening meal unless you feel you can't spend the night outside, which would be the wisest place to sleep. Thank you."

The schoolroom, which still had blackboards on the walls, emptied. Every commander tried shouting louder than the others as he summoned his squad. The hubbub that accompanied the dispatching of each nomad squad had a certain distinction: rank no longer counted. If a sergeant was in charge of a squad and an officer was assigned to it, the officer had to take the sergeant's orders. That was the rule of the Black Commandos. It accentuated the daring character of the venture—and it gave the sergeants a big kick.

It was time to start. From the spot where the trucks were going to drop us, on the road at the foot of the *jebel*, it was still a three-hour march, over difficult tracks, to the *mechta* where our squad was to make its first contact: Sidi Salem.

The embarkation and the drive in an escorted convoy were soon over. Our little squads were quietly dropped off at intervals along the road.

Company Sergeant-Major Peisson led the way. I marched beside him.

We began the slow ascent of a dried-up, deserted *wadi* bed between bushy heights. After so many hours of noisy collective life in the regiment, on the company parade ground, in the trucks, we were sobered once again by the silence and solitude of this nomad work. Freed from the armored shell with which "pacification" has covered the whole surface of the immense country, we were re-entering the warm interior of Algeria.

2/ The climb to the *mechta* was no fun. Toward nightfall, about two miles from Sidi Salem, a burst of fire coming from nowhere in particular and immediately followed by another—they are always impossible to pinpoint—halted our march.

Nomadization was getting off to a rough start. Not that we hadn't expected as much; our commandos had infuriated the *fellagha*, who had sworn to cut the experiment short. They had planned to do so by liquidating some of the Arabs who had invited us into their homes too freely, as had happened the previous week after our visit to Bou Segha. They also hoped to wipe out one of our squads—which they had not so far achieved.

The two bursts of fire probably indicated the beginning of an engagement that might well be a tough one.

But scarcely had we begun to take extended order when a hailstorm more violent than any of us had ever seen burst over our heads. With hailstones as big as fists, the storm cleared the hillside as effectively as any artillery could have done. The hailstorm gave place to a downpour of rain, and when we emerged from shelter under the rocks, we could find neither the *fellagha* nor any sign of tracks.

By taking compass bearings we got back to our route, but it was after nightfall when we arrived, soaked to the skin, at the *mechta* of Sidi Salem.

Omar Saïd, who was apparently head of the tribe, had been described by our intelligence officer as the local intellectual, probably in touch with the FLN and classified as a fellow traveler. He was astonished to see our squad turn up in such a sad state. But he knew our Black Commandos—he had seen them once a month earlier—so he agreed to bring us whatever clothing he could find in three or four old painted wooden chests of his. Then he led us into the dryest room in his mud house, where we took off our soaking uniforms. We emerged as a band of many-colored—but dry—pirates.

At Sidi Salem/ Company Sergeant-Major Peisson, round-headed and barrel-chested, was seated on a stool in a corner of the low mud room. He was draped in a flowing white Arab robe, and the black flannel band around his waist was all that remained of the commando uniform. Stolid as ever, he seemed deeply absorbed as the little candle, the only light in the room, threw his fantastic shadow on the cracked walls. His appearance suggested a monk strayed from the pages of Rabelais.

The other drowned rats of the squadron were just as strangely dressed. Each of us had got himself up somehow with odds and ends from our hosts' wardrobe.

We had been waiting for an hour now.

We were all seated or reclining, waiting for some invisible women to finish their elaborate culinary preparations. Omar had told them to make a *couscous* for us.

Omar brought into the little room, one after another, three young men who had more of a peasant look than he did, and introduced them as his brothers. They were muffled up in woolen *kachabias* and sat cross-legged, taciturn and cowed. Conversation was laborious to a degree. Omar was very reserved, while the other three remained completely silent, contenting themselves with staring at us. From time to time, one of them would go out. Then he would come back and sit down, in the same place, without a word.

Peisson had stationed Sergeant Kopf, looking like a clown in baggy royal-blue trousers and a patched red jersey, at the entrance of the courtyard. As far as possible and without being too obvious, he was supposed to serve as a lookout.

"Say, chief, can't he show us the house? It would pass the time." Geronimo, who was lying on the ground and whittling away at an olive branch with his dagger, did not like doing nothing. Probably, too, he thought that where there were so many men, there must be some women. And not necessarily so dried up as the old hag who had brought us some dry cakes and plates of dry corn while we were waiting; indeed, her withered breasts looked as if they could form part of the menu.

Peisson's silence was regal. He was there to "make contact," and he meant to make contact. If anyone wanted to play around, he would have to look elsewhere. He turned to our young interpreter, Ben Ali.

"Ask him if he's pleased with the crops."

Ben Ali translated the question for Omar.

"*Ch-ou-ia* . . . *Ch-ou-ia,*" Omar vouchsafed slowly, putting the accent on the *ou*.

Silence fell again.

The other men, the brothers, were chewing herbs without budging an inch. One of them got up, went out, and shut the door softly.

"Again! Have they got to piss every ten minutes, these guys?" said the delighted Geronimo.

Peisson turned to the interpreter. "Ask him if he's got enough to eat for all his family at this time of year, or if he needs anything."

The interpreter translated.

Omar, who had remained standing, solemnly took **one**

hand out of his sleeve. He pulled slightly at his *kachabia,* which was less patched than those of the others, to make it fall better over his right foot, and then slowly thrust both hands back into his ample sleeves. He ventured the smallest of dry smiles and opened his mouth as little as possible.

"*Ch-ou-ia . . . Ch-ou-ia . . .*"

There was silence once more.

It did not look as though the evening were going to be as exciting as our mountain trip, nor as interesting as Peisson had hoped. He began, indeed, to be a little uneasy. There were four strong young Arabs in the room, and the atmosphere was one of evident hostility. The reports on Omar's state of mind had been disquieting, and then those bursts of fire in the afternoon . . . How many Arabs were in the neighboring houses?

Peisson cast a searching glance at our weapons. Geronimo, a creature of habit even in the faded robe he was wearing, still had his tommy-gun hanging around his neck. Kopf was outside with his. Peisson had his rifle under his feet—that was all right. The three other rifles were hanging on the wall, within arm's reach.

A volley of knocks on one of the wooden doors in the courtyard tore into the heavy silence. With one bound Geronimo, dropping his dagger and olive branch and grasping his tommy-gun, was out in the courtyard, rushing to the aid of Kopf. The interpreter and Canu got up and started toward their rifles.

In a voice that was cold and decisive, Peisson stopped them. "Keep calm. Don't lose your heads. Stay put."

He had not stirred an inch. His eyes alone explored the dark hole of night beyond the door, which Geronimo had left open.

In the same tone of voice he continued:

"If you're going to be so jumpy, you should have stayed home. There's a man on guard, and that's enough, see? The others are here to talk, see?"

Peisson's calm was impressive. There was no doubt that he had what it takes.

Peisson was probably nearing fifty. He was an accountant in the nationalized French Electricity Corporation at Montpellier, the father of a family and a peaceable bureaucrat. He had been called up, as had all of us, but he had been called for a definite job: Staff Company Sergeant-Major. The post is a sort of secretaryship to a unit in the field; it requires a certain competence in paper work, which explains why old Peisson had been drafted "out of his class." Before his draft notice had been signed, he had been asked whether he was willing to go, and he had agreed.

When we returned from an operation, fagged out after hours of marching and sometimes excited over a skirmish, we took it for granted that we would find Daddy Peisson, wearing just an undershirt over his hairy chest, with an unlighted cigarette dangling from his lips, tidying up his papers and preparing files for the colonel or Henry to sign. He was always sitting in his camp chair behind a rickety bridge table, struggling with a sputtering field telephone, and he had become for us a sort of symbol of the head of the household. To return to Peisson was like returning home, with supper and bed waiting.

When the commando squads were being formed, nobody had thought for a moment of asking Peisson to join— after all, you don't ask your mother to go and run the hundred-yard dash for you. And Peisson would have been the last to think of himself for this work.

But on Saturday, in the regimental NCO mess, a discussion that had started up quietly suddenly turned nasty.

Sergeant Brique and his friend Valaud, who always volunteered for every tough job, had started yelling.

"These Black Commandos—balls! I'm fed up with the whole idea. We didn't come here to suck up to the gooks. To hell with it!"

"That goes for me, too! I've had it! They're going to think we're goddam fools. The little rats knock us off at point-blank range, and then we've got to go and tell them bedtime stories. Well, I'll tell you one thing: if we go on with this nonsense, we're finished. With this sort of country, there's only one thing that'll keep 'em quiet—the big stick. If they see us brown-nosing around, playing footsie with them, and all this lovey-dovey stuff, there'll be no holding 'em. We're finished, I tell you. The colonel can take his Black Commandos and stuff 'em."

It was not the first time these two NCO's and one or two others had said what they thought of the commando experiment. Up to now, however, they had not had the face to withdraw from the commandos, or even to campaign against them too openly. Most of our men didn't much care, but they were, if anything, in favor of the plan.

On Saturday night, however, it was a different matter. There had been a new and particularly horrible ambush, and some men had been viciously mutilated. A wave of resentment had swept through the troops, and they were in the mood for a gook-hunt. Brique and Valaud had seen their chance, and ever since the meal started they had been knocking the "give-them-candy boys," the "sob sisters," the "ass-kissers"—meaning the Black Commandos.

The campaign was having its effect.

Peisson, the senior NCO, was presiding over the mess in silence as usual. Although he said nothing, he was watching. Studying the various faces, noting an air of hesitation here, a questioning look there, and the new respect with which the two sergeants' braggadocio was greeted, he recognized that a disaster was threatening. It was quite possible that the next morning not a single NCO would volunteer to go out with the commando squads.

Peisson continued to wait.

The triumph of the attackers was becoming clearer every moment. Tomorrow morning it would almost certainly be too late.

Peisson took out a cigarette, calmly lighted it, and took advantage of a brief pause to intervene.

"Personally, I know nothing about your politics, see? But the commandos—it's the best damn thing we've done around here, and if you want to ditch them, all I can say is it's a stinking thing to do. Me, I'm volunteering to go out with them. Get it?"

The astonishment was as universal as Peisson had expected. Not a soul dared to say a word more on a subject so explosive that it had just blown a regimental institution to smithereens. Brique and Valaud were so thoroughly routed that even they went back to their commando jobs.

That was why Peisson was out with us now, for the first time.

Kopf and Geronimo appeared in the doorway. Each of them was holding one arm of a young Arab, a lively muscular boy with a flat nose, brown fuzzy hair, and a quick-witted manner that showed little sign of fright. They had a firm grip on him.

Omar's face changed. His attitude of contemptuous indifference dropped from him as he started toward the young man. But he stopped, pulled himself together, and turned to Peisson, talking rapidly.

"Chief, tell them to let him go. It's my son—Ahmed, my son. Come on, chief!"

"Let him go, you two. You can see for yourselves he can't do you any harm. I wonder when you're going to learn how to behave in someone else's house. He's told you it's his son. Get it?"

Peisson was sarcastic. But, all the same, he was relieved; he had had a scare. It was not very amusing to imagine what would happen in this *mechta* at the end of the world, cut off from radio contact by the storm that was still raging, if there were some real trouble.

Omar, who had showed in his agitation that he knew a little French, had thawed a little. Peisson's calm had impressed him, too. He turned to the interpreter and launched into a long story, waving his arms and gesticulating with a gusto all the more astonishing because he had been like a statue for the last hour and a half.

Ben Ali translated.

"He says his son was nearly killed by the troops last month. They took him for a *fellagha*, and he got a bayonet jab in the right leg, and they were going to finish him off. . . . He says he tried every way he could to see the gendarmes to get him out of prison because he was innocent and all that. . . . But the cops wouldn't even listen to him, they sent him away every time and told him that if he came back they'd hang him, too. . . . He says that the Kouiba cops are bastards and it's always like that. He says his son is seventeen, and he's the baker's delivery boy, and that he's never meddled with politics, and he's no more a *fellagha* than you or me (in a manner of speaking). . . . Then he says that nobody wanted to listen to him. He went to the municipal buildings, but the mayor told a gendarme to say that he hadn't got any time to waste seeing a Communist. . . . He says he's not a Communist at all, and they say that to annoy him. It was the neighbor who told the gendarmes that last year. The neighbor he'd lost a donkey and he thought Omar had stolen it. . . . But he's not a Communist, or anything at all, he's not interested in politics. . . . Then he says his son was going to die, and if that happened, he and all his brothers would become *fellagha*, and the gendarmes, they're bastards. . . . Then some chaps in black like us came along, and he told them they were bastards, too, and that his son was going to be killed. The chief of the boys in black (that must have been Baral, from what I can make out) told him that he'd get his son back for him. Then he gave our boys dinner. . . . And his son came back the next week. . . . He says that's why he asked us in this evening, but he's not very keen on having us in, because the *fellagha*, they thought it was funny that he'd got his son back like that, and they made it known that if he'd turned into a traitor and a spy for the French, they'd cut his throat and his son's, too. . . . So he'd like it better if we didn't come here too much. . . . But he's glad they've given him back his son, and, what with the storm, he thinks the *fellagha* won't come tonight . . . so he's asked us in."

When Ben Ali had finished translating, Omar, who had become positively loquacious, started to talk again. He was interrupted by the entry of two women in many-colored robes of old satin, carrying two enormous wooden bowls filled with *couscous*. Peisson looked at the *couscous* hungrily, Geronimo and Kopf at the young women. Peisson glared at Geronimo and Kopf. "Watch it, you two. We're not here for that."

We did our best to sit down on the ground around the huge dish on the low table without sticking our feet into the serving-dish; it was not easy. The women had disappeared, the four Arabs remained standing, and young Ahmed had sat down in the farthest corner, sulking.

"Ask them to come and eat with us," Peisson told the interpreter, who translated.

The atmosphere had definitely changed. They came and sat down beside us. All the same, Omar's sharp eye and haughty look made us feel a little uncomfortable.

"Maybe he's not a Communist—we don't know anything about that—but I'll bet he's no angel either, eh?" Kopf whispered into Peisson's ear.

Peisson was thinking just about the same thing. And Omar's dictatorial little gestures ordering his brothers to sit down or get up and his son to go out suggested nothing of the country bumpkin. He was no longer silent; on the contrary, he was talkative. But he was difficult to figure out, a worrying, complex, human individual.

Peisson profited from the growing friendliness to give the conversation a new turn. "Then he must be pleased with our troops—ask him what he thinks of them."

Ben Ali translated. Once more Omar talked for a long time.

"Condense that a bit. Otherwise, we'll never be finished."

"He says no. Because five times now he's been pulled in in roundups, and every time they keep him in the jug for days without asking him any questions and then let him go without saying a thing. . . . He says he's had enough of it. . . . He says that the last time he was in the jug three days without eating. . . . He's belly-aching, see? He looks a bit of a belly-acher, anyway. I haven't got much use for this guy, personally. I like the others better."

Kopf, who had apparently become prey to some strong emotion, hastily swallowed the enormous shovelful of *couscous* he had in his mouth and waved his arms to show that he wanted to speak. He began to talk in his magnificent Alsatian accent, which never failed to enchant us. His great friendly face was contorted with grimaces worthy of his effort to make Arabs understand the French of Strasbourg.

"Tell him that if he's so soft he can't go three days without eating, he isn't a man. You can tell him I went fifteen days without eating—except for a rat every other day—and my balls freezing in the snow, and I nearly conked out, but I made it. And you can tell him . . ."

Kopf ended the hair-raising account of his sufferings, and Ben Ali translated it to the Arab audience. Their astonishment and admiration increased visibly as the story went on. I looked at Sergeant Kopf, a pillar of the regiment, a soldier who was conscientious, brave, and always obliging—one of the ones who were nicest to the Arabs. And with the same wonder that I always felt, I saw him again before the icy gates of Stalingrad, in a veritable hell of fire and famine. He had been a young conscript of sixteen whom the *Wehrmacht* had rounded up in Alsace, and he had fought manfully, winning the Iron Cross that he wore on his SS uniform. Good old Kopf, that poor son-of-a-gun.

"And there were times I did guard duty at night with the thermometer at twenty-five below, and me with nothing to eat all day, and I did it just the same. Ask him if he and his Communist pals would have done the same."

"But he's told you he's not a Communist."

"It's all the same to me—I don't particularly care whether he's a Communist or not—but ask him if they'd have done the same!"

Everyone laughed.

Geronimo had disappeared. He had whispered a few words to one of Omar's brothers and then gone out with him.

The other soldier, Canu, a timid, serious, gentle boy, dived happily into the *couscous* in silence; he had not eaten so well for a long time. He was reminded of his little mountain farm in the Pyrenees, and he withdrew into himself, thinking of his wife and daughter. Every time he saw a jug of milk, he thought of his family. He would take a picture of them out of his jacket and look sad.

Geronimo came back with a little boy in his arms. The Arab who had gone out with him to find the child looked at Omar a little nervously, as if to excuse himself. But Omar was more relaxed than ever. If Geronimo wanted to see a kid, why not?

Geronimo adored children. Often you would have to go and pull him away, right in the middle of a village street, where he might squat for half an hour at a time making funny faces, trying to delight the little Arab children, who were afraid of him. I realized suddenly that this was the first time I had ever seen him without his tommy-gun. He had left it in the corner and forgotten all about it. His handsome dark head was ribbed by the shadows thrown from the two candles that lighted the room. He was the young French hero of the pacification campaign, the kind you see on posters. Omar watched him with a smile that was almost benevolent.

Through the welter of misunderstandings and memories, of deaths and bitternesses, of crimes and mistrust, in the warmth of this little mud room a contact had been made. Ahmed's painful thigh wound and the horrible remembrance of Marcus's body and Geronimo's accident, Palestro and Stalingrad, the incomprehensible folly of men, the vanity of politics, the value of human beings—so many feelings were jumbled together in this strange moment. The sensation was probably a useless one that likely enough would lead nowhere, but its immediacy and the reality of it swept away all analysis. The Arabs had become men—and the soldiers had become men.

Peisson never lost sight of the things that mattered. It was nearly midnight and soon it would be time to go to sleep. This was a delicate issue.

There could be no question of sleeping out of doors, as the colonel had recommended in his last-minute instructions; the mountain was deluged. We had no choice but to sleep in the *mechta*. Omar had said that the *fellagha* would not come because of the storm. But perhaps Omar was in with the rebels. And the storm, after all, had stopped.

It seemed sensible to take the routine precautions: to have two men on guard the whole time, with arms at the ready. But Omar and his brothers, who had become so friendly and apparently sincere, had already invited us all to sleep there in the room with them. They said that they would guard us. To refuse meant that we would undo all the good that had been done. We would be offending our hosts, hurting them deeply. With one stroke we would rebuild the wall of hostility that we had encountered when we arrived. But to accept?

Peisson added things up: in any case, the Arabs in the room were not armed. If they wanted to get arms or to call the *fellagha*, one of them would have to go out through the room's only door. All Peisson had to do was take up a position so that he could put his legs across the doorway.

"Chief, you want to sleep? Don't worry, I guard. Everyone sleep quiet. You're in my house," said Omar.

Everyone started to make himself at home. There was not much space left on the floor. Omar put his mat on the dresser and lay down there. We opened our sleeping-bags and took off our shoes.

Omar had settled down, but he was not yet asleep. He looked around the room, with its unaccustomed bustle. He was waiting until everyone was ready for the night before he blew out the candle.

From the Jebel Kerrouch to the Wadi Ahmar, in twenty different mountain *mechtas*, our men were probably getting into their sleeping-bags at about that moment, with the confused but deeply felt sensation that they were at the very heart of this strange war. As they lay side by side with the other men, they had no way of telling who might be enemies or who might be friends. To put oneself into a frame of mind confident enough for sleep requires a real effort at self-control. This silent struggle within each individual is perhaps the real battle for Algeria.

Omar gave a last look around. His face had resumed its impenetrable mask. He saw the company sergeant-major's feet sticking out toward the door and barring access to it. His gaze traveled the full length of Peisson, and their eyes met. Peisson pulled in his feet, doubling up his legs at the knees to leave the door free. Omar looked at the door, and the smallest of smiles appeared at the corner of his mouth. He blew out the candle. And Peisson stretched out his feet to bar the door again.

"Good night, Omar . . . Good night . . ."

"Ah . . . *Ch-ou-ia* . . ."

3/ In the old garage-messroom, where it was now cold of a morning, Espanieul and Julienne, in pajama trousers and fur-lined jackets, were finishing their breakfast coffee and casting a casual glance at the *Journal d'Alger*—of the day before. When you have the feeling that you are at the heart of a problem, you lose interest in the way the daily news presents only the surfaces.

Geronimo and I had come down from the mountains in order to attend our meeting, and when Espanieul saw us enter he gave an exclamation of pleasure; every time he saw me with Geronimo, we struck him as an odd pair. He was not the only one who thought so. All the same, Geronimo was the best bodyguard on a ticklish expedition.

After one or two well-worn jokes about the hybrid

unions this war had brought about, Espanieul said in a more serious tone:

"So you've seen Omar Saïd?"

"Yes. You couldn't call him a comedian."

"So they tell me. But he's got a head on his shoulders, that guy. And if we could break the bastard down, it'd have an effect in the area."

"Maybe. But in that case it'd have been better not to lock him up twice a month, starve him, carve up his son— friendly tricks like that."

"We've given him back his son. Anyway, that's all past history: he can see for himself we're making an effort now. Is it O.K. by him to take us to the Moorish café?"

"We haven't got that far. Peisson's trying to prepare the ground."

Espanieul told Julienne one of our plans: to send three of our men to the Moorish café at Kouiba one Sunday to try to sound out the local leaders. To bring it off, we had to persuade one of the Arabs to take us there, which meant a considerable risk for him if things went sour.

But all that was another matter. Today we had work at Algiers.

Espanieul looked at his watch. He hadn't shaved yet, and neither had Julienne. We would be two hours on the road—it was high time we got ready.

"I've got an appointment with our gallant and eminent commander-in-chief in person at eleven o'clock," Espanieul said. "We'll drop Julienne at the Algiers division. His job is to help himself to whatever he can lay his hands on for our squads. And you I'm dropping at the GG. O.K.? It'll be a big deal."

The jaunt was not simply for the pleasure Espanieul always derived from stirring up the civil and military institutions of the State. Our tenuous experiment was at stake in these visits to the "bureaucracy"—whether the brass would continue or defeat our Black Commandos. Espanieul, who knew what he was doing, for all his mad-dog ways, was constantly at work defending our activity and mustering support for it. Because such experiments question the whole structure of the military protection of Algeria, the Black Commandos had become the focal point for a real test of strength. And this underground struggle had taken on an almost official air the day that all the top brass of Algeria (four generals, six colonels, the Minister Resident, and his personal staff) had come down in a convoy of helicopters to get a firsthand view of our commandos and their work.

That was the day I had met M. Robert Lacoste.

Espanieul had already had a long interview with Lacoste. They had hit it off. The colonel had been delighted by their first conversation.

"He's a good Joe," Espanieul had told us. "He absolutely agrees with us. He thinks the present military routine is a lot of shit (his language is very colorful, by the way). All these swollen units, the roundups, the phony operations, the hundreds of so-called suspects that they either don't know what to do with or they knock off, the generals who get their kicks out of the war . . . In fact, he thinks exactly like us. I didn't even need to convince him. He knew it all. And he told me that our ideas on the commandos were just what he wanted, that that was what 'pacification' ought to be—and that he'd help us."

Espanieul had asked the Minister to show his support personally by coming down and seeing our commandos on the spot. Hence the inspection.

I was naturally curious about this meeting.

Robert Lacoste, for me, was two superimposed pictures that didn't gibe—and I did not know which was the right one.

He was the Socialist deputy whom I had often seen at a conference table: he was all instinct, close to the people; he seemed to have a feeling for popular sentiment and was able to cut through political verbiage with incisive common sense.

He was also the proconsul—an unlooked-for side of his character which meanwhile was being revealed by radio and newspapers. The second Lacoste was as confident and as commanding in his manner as the first was simple. He was apparently as satisfied with the jingoism of his speeches as the other was distrustful of official propaganda. The new Lacoste, as militaristic as the generals, as "France is here to stay" as the die-hards, gave the impression of being the contrary of the first rather than his protraction.

Which of the two pictures was the real likeness of the man who now represented France in Algeria?

Neither.

The Minister who had had a sandwich that day on a peak in the south of Algeria was no longer the down-to-earth politician of the Dordogne. But he was even less the Caesar of pacification.

He had drawn us into a corner of the tent where so much rank was in evidence and confided to us in a modest and embarrassed fashion what he had already told Espanieul. He wanted to break with the relentless machinery that was transforming our army, for the greater satisfaction of the FLN extremists, into an army of occupation—but how was he to bring it off? How could one reach the Moslem masses rationally instead of using terror? In Africa the Minister Resident was far less precise and concrete than the Socialist of the old days. The farmers and the workers among his constituents at home were human beings whom he knew how to appreciate and how to handle. But the Arabs seemed scarcely men to him, as remote from the world of his Algiers palace as the Eskimos of the North Pole.

That was why an experiment such as ours, disliked as it was by certain military leaders, seemed to him a card worth playing. And the language Lacoste chose to express his opinion of these generals was as unprintable as the epithets of a drill sergeant. When he left, he suggested that we come and see him personally in Algiers so that he could help us—as much as he could.

In the black staff car that was taking us to Algiers, Espanieul filled in the big picture for us and cleared his own mind by summing up our remaining chances of withstanding the growing hostile pressures.

"The fellows at the GG and Minister himself aren't bad, but I'm losing confidence in them. I don't doubt that they're properly zeroed in. But they don't seem to have the guts to face up to anyone. Mention a general . . . 'Generals? Messing around with them means nothing but trouble!' Behind the generals' backs these characters in the Ministry say things ten times worse than anything we'd think of saying, but they wouldn't lift a little finger to give the generals an order. It makes no sense—they're groveling in front of the myth of the army. Mention the mayors . . . 'The mayors? Listen, friend, you don't know what you're saying. If we rub *them* the wrong way, it'll be civil war here.' These Ministry guys will throw mud all over the place and tell you the army brass are a bunch of bastards who've put us in the position we're in today. At the same time they hide behind the army, trembling at the idea that the very militiamen they armed and turned over to the mayors will start shooting up the place in broad daylight. . . . You're telling me! So far they've only been doing it at night."

Julienne listened to Espanieul with interest. He was surprised at the second-rateness of men "in power." He had never in his life met a Minister or even a First Secretary. In this respect, he had retained a very "Third Republic" mentality; he had no illusions about the lack of dedication among office-holders, but he was convinced that they had the power to do big things, either good or bad. Actually, the opposite is true: they are more honest than most people imagine, but are ineffectual. And Espanieul knew this. Even so, he had been stupefied to discover, very soon after his first interview with the Minister, that although the Minister was pressing buzzers all day long, there was a short circuit in the system.

"He dictates very impressive directives, which are carefully printed and widely distributed. So what? People couldn't care less. And nothing happens. I told him so. These grotesque operations, with five thousand men, artillery, fighter support—every time one of them happens, there's hell to pay. In one fell swoop all the efforts we've made to re-establish contact with the population are undone. He agrees one hundred per cent, he says, and he'll go even further—'But how do you expect me to stop them?' I told him: 'Bypass three particularly stupid generals and you'll have the whole army behind you!' 'Look, pal, there's nothing I'd like better! But I can't. It doesn't depend on me.' His colleagues in Paris told me exactly the same thing: it didn't depend on them, either."

Julienne interrupted: "Maybe he couldn't do anything about the generals. But the gendarmerie, the mayors, the public corporations, the money—he could try something, couldn't he?"

Espanieul shrugged his shoulders. The conversation reminded him of his own disappointments, the futility of his previous contacts with people on whom, in theory, Algeria depended. Suddenly he was seeing this latest expedition as just another waste of time.

"It seems not," Espanieul grumbled. "That doesn't depend on him, either. There's always one reason or another why people can't do something about the situation. Nothing depends on anyone."

The car was crossing Maison Carrée, the big Algiers suburb that is a refuge for all the terrorist cells that have been tracked down in the capital itself and would be too exposed in the countryside.

The crowds swarming in the streets forced us to slow down to walking pace. The uproar of the town was a contrast to the solitude of our posts, the calm of our mountains. Once more we experienced, as one always does when entering a city from the country, the desperate feeling that men's fate is only partially decided on the spot where they fight, and that the real decisions are made in the anonymous capitals, where the underground tug-of-war between the big interests determines the pattern of collective life.

Julienne, in the rear seat of the Citroën, leaned back and relaxed, making the most of this entr'acte. He was stimulated by the sight of the crowd of Arabs and Europeans, mingling, going about their apparently peaceful business, and he thought about Espanieul's experiences.

"There's one question that stands out. The political authorities are powerless—I should say, nonexistent—in the face of the forces that gravitate around them—the army, big money, the civil service. I'll grant you that. But then these feudal powers themselves must have some kind of aim, they must have a policy. What is it? That's the question: what is it? Certainly one doesn't see it."

"There's nothing to see. An aim, yes. A policy? No. Everyone is defending his own interests as best he can, which isn't very well, and beyond that he just hopes that things will work out by themselves. Nothing more. The journalists are repeating like idiots that the army may be about to carry out a *coup d'état,* to 'seize power.' Hell, that's for the birds! What are the army brass interested in? Most of them in their promotion; in the ten billion francs of blocked credits which may mean the staff fifteen-horsepower Citroëns won't be replaced by the new model; and in newspaper stories—so they can see their names in print. Seizing power? It hasn't entered their heads. That's for the scum. The rest? They'd give half their pay, cash down, if the political leaders would only give them directives and shoulder the responsibilities."

Espanieul and I were still thinking of a recent dramatic conversation we had had with an unusual general who was in command of the operational area where we had been sent on a special mission. He was a forthright, courageous man, still obsessed by what had happened in Indochina. He told us:

"I've only got one problem, but it takes in all the others. I put it up to them at Algiers every time I go there. Nothing doing—nobody will answer me. It's this: our intelligence is pretty good in this area—I know who the principal suspects are, I know their networks, the political commissioners, those actively sympathetic with the FLN. Good. Now, what do I do?

"If I don't arrest them, they continue their work of political and administrative infiltration, which is very efficient and much more of a threat to the future than the armed bands. What's the use of staying here, tracking down a few hunting guns in the mountains, if we let them operate like that under our very noses?

"O.K., I arrest them. Then what's going to happen? Since there will be no precise charges, no statutory offenses to charge them with, one day or other, after a not very pleasant period in a prison or a camp, they'll be released. Then they'll come back here as political martyrs, with their prestige ten times higher. That's all they want. They'll have won a round. And if there are elections, you can guess the outcome!

"O.K. What's the answer? Arrest them and knock them off? It's the only reasonable solution. Only wait a minute. I'm not going to do that without an *order*. In Algiers they tell me that they don't want to know anything, that they'll shut their eyes. Of course they will. They get the dirty work done by the troops and they're rid of the nationalist ring-leaders, and then one fine day they turn on the army and say it's butchery. But those gentlemen will have kept their own hands clean. Well, I'm not playing that game. What I say is: 'If you want me to arrest them and knock them off, give me the order to do it. After all, who's responsible? The Government, damn it! And if not, have the guts to say so! But make up your minds.'

"Because, let me tell you, those gentlemen keep their consciences clear by respecting the lives of a few ringleaders in an area like this, and then, a year later, do you know what happens? They open up with artillery against women and children because the whole tribe has gone over to the guer-rillas. That's what they had me do in Indochina. I'm not starting the same thing over again!

"Well, now, what *am* I supposed to do? Ten times—do you hear?—it's ten times now that I've asked for instructions from the Government-General. No answer. They don't want to know about it."

This particular general worshipped De Lattre ("that man knew how to command"). He told us half a dozen different ways that he was ready to carry out any policy, if only there was one. He couldn't stop talking about what he called the cowardice of the political leaders.

To complete our education, he took us to see a neighbor, a colonel commanding another operational area. He wanted to show us a few more significant details.

The colonel was in a special location—one of those showplace areas where they take parliamentary delegates on tour when they come over to carry out "inquiries" in Algeria.

Among other things in the showplace was a map of villages regained, a map "specially prepared for the Minister's staff." The real map was stashed away in a drawer. There was also a plan of the fifty-thousand-acre agricultural property which, according to reports, had been distributed to Moslems "as part of the agrarian reform," and of which not a square inch had yet been given to any Moslem. And so forth.

The general concluded: "They want us to give them propaganda. I've no objection if it helps them carry out a policy. But what policy? Nobody'll answer that one. And they're letting the army get fouled up, to turn into a super-police, which makes us sick. It'll come to no good, believe me."

Our car had reached Algiers, the capital of the war—the capital, indeed, of France, for the history of the whole country is being written there.

Chapter Two

1/ After our discussions at Headquarters and the Government-General, it became clear that the activities of our Black Commandos would eventually lose official support. But this meant only the end of an illusion; the real difficulties lay elsewhere, and were just beginning.

We had succeeded, as we had hoped, in thawing out the Arab world, which we continued to penetrate, almost to shape somewhat, by means of our small nomad squads living in its midst. But this very success, as it was easy to foresee, had not left the rebels indifferent: they found it intolerable. If they did not strike back, they would lose political control of the area. After a period during which the number of incidents (roads destroyed, buildings burned, plantations sacked) had steadily decreased, we discovered from the usual signs that a new rebel team had been sent in to get the people in hand for a counterattack. Gradually the incidents started up again.

A well-planned and daring ambush, less than a mile from the headquarters of one of our battalions, had resulted in giving a lift to the *fellagha*'s prestige and had shaken the conviction, still tenuous among our men, that daily, tireless, thorough, and confident contact with the Arabs was the most effective and probably the only way of fighting.

The casualties in the ambush had been a second lieutenant and a sergeant, both seriously wounded. The officer was a newcomer and not well known, so his loss did not leave much of a mark. But the sergeant was Brique—one of the stars of the regiment.

Brique was detested by some people but attractive to most. He had a reputation for going after a fight with a tommy-gun or with his bare fists, and the news about him caused a sensation. Everyone knew his mustache, his way of sometimes using incomprehensible Latin words to suggest the profundity of his ideas, his success with the daughter of the village plumber. He was someone. He left a gap, and through the gap began to seep once more the virus of mistrust.

All the more easily because Brique had always been contemptuous of the plan. "These Black Commandos, they make us look like a bunch of dumb bastards. While we're giving them the big smile, the gooks are thinking up dirty tricks behind our backs. The less you keep an eye on them, the more likely you are to have your face pushed in. . . . I'm telling you, you'll see."

Now the sight of him with his chest bashed in, which many of the men had been able to see in the farmyard where he was waiting for the ambulance from the Kouiba hospital, had given Brique a power of persuasion far more effective than when he could still talk. The urge for vengeance was beginning to create havoc again.

Espanieul had sensed what was at stake after Brique's ambush. He had come down personally to cope with the excitement and to insist on discipline: there must be no reprisals. He himself had staged an operation that night to track down the Arabs responsible for the attack, and, on the whole, he had ensured that our troops did not fire at everything they saw. The first round had been won.

The second phase was harder: to stir up once again enough volunteers so that our commandos could continue their nomadization. Our mission was by nature trustful of the people around us, some of whom we knew—but, as always, which ones?—must have helped by hiding and covering for the instigators of the ambush.

With firm handling, the situation had been restored. A number of the early volunteers had now become so embittered that they just gave up. But others agreed to try the experiment—out of friendship for one of the NCO's or simply for the sake of a change of pace.

Or perhaps they were even more deeply motivated by their disgust at the vulgar racialism of the worst rabble-rousers, and felt basically drawn toward this poor, distant race. Many of our own troops did come to feel a confused sense of solidarity with the Arab people in the face of the even more foreign interests that seemed to rule both worlds.

Only a month earlier, Company Sergeant-Major Peisson had silenced a diatribe against the Black Commandos with the uncalled-for gesture (in view of his age and position) of volunteering for the outfit himself. This time it was Gambert who led the counterattack, with methods of his own.

The day after the ambush, Sergeant Valaud, who belonged to Gambert's commando squad and who was a good talker, wound up a long harangue after dinner by declaring: "Well, boys, all we've got to do now is to pay them back for Brique and give them a beating they'll never forget. As for going back and sucking up to them, I'd as soon get my balls caught in a wringer."

Gambert waited for him to finish, and then said: "Tough luck! You'll have them caught anyway because you're coming back on commando with me, and, what's more, tomorrow! See?"

"Never!"

"Never?"

"Never!"

"Say that again!"

Valaud had no choice. His prestige was based on his ability to express himself better than most of the men. To give in intellectually to Gambert, to turn around and contradict himself at a minute's interval, would be sheer suicide. It was out of the question.

"Never!"

That was the last word. With one well-placed, deadly punch, Gambert laid the sergeant out on the mess floor. He then cast a questioning glance around at the others. It was an old trick of his—making certain, by throwing down a silent challenge, that nobody else wanted to take him on.

The day was won. It was not exactly that the men were afraid—some of them were stronger than Gambert, or at least his equal. But they were caught off guard. Physical force, when it is used to serve what is considered an intellectual cause, has amazing power. In this respect, Gambert was irreplaceable. Every detail of his appearance and his character corresponded to the classic picture of the bully and the gook-hunter. And because he had deliberately chosen the opposite path, he had become a conspicuous paradox—a trump card for the Black Commandos. They needed one.

An Evening at Headquarters/ It was six o'clock in the evening. The Algerian winter sun, lowering and red as molten iron, filled the little room in the headquarters where Jouve was duty officer. His light bushy hair and fair complexion seemed even more dazzling beside the Black Angel, who had become Jouve's faithful bodyguard. These two got on well together. Jouve, president of the Ex-Servicemen's Association of his little town near Toulouse, and a national figure in one of the big parties, was used to handling men. He knew just how to make Geronimo feel good. And Geronimo responded with a fond admiration that Jouve appreciated.

Nothing in particular had happened. The day was just ending. Captain Jouve, tall and well built, dressed in a brand-new camouflage uniform with the rosette of the Legion of Honor over the left breast pocket, was standing in front of the little window, his hands in his belt. Along the distant horizon he saw a fine line, a little darker than the sky, a little paler than the earth, which was the Mediterranean. He was in his element, standing just where he should be, on the battlements of civilization.

"We'll get them, Geronimo—we'll get them yet."

The Black Angel took one of his eternal caramels out of his pocket and began to munch it. "Of course, sir, but when?"

"Don't you worry. It'll take time, but they won't get away with it, those Arabs. I told them so in Paris. There they agree with me. Childish stuff like these Black Commandos is no damn good. Matter of fact, it only encourages the bastards. And it makes the honest Frenchmen puke; here they only ask one thing—that the army defend them against murderers. They don't ask the army to try and outsmart the gooks by sucking up to them. You've got to be a phony like Julie to play that game. The colonel's completely foxed: he's fond of Julie because he thinks he's funny—I can't see it myself. But we'll open his eyes in the end."

Geronimo was happy in his gloom. His fingers felt the comforting contact of his nice clean tommy-gun, slung around his neck as usual. If he could follow such a man as Jouve, perhaps there was justification for his mobilization after all.

Like all those who distrusted the Black Commandos, Captain Jouve, whether consciously or not, felt the need for a target. He had chosen Captain Julienne, or "Julie," as he was called. And spontaneously a protective armor had grown up around Julienne to keep him from sticking his neck out.

The pattern is now only too familiar in Algeria. Any genuine attempt to make contact with the Arabs—and the army of Africa has made numerous attempts—arouses first skepticism, then a growing distrust, and finally, if it takes root, open hostility. In our area it was the Black Commandos, and somewhere else another method was tried, but the principle is always the same. What matters is the common idea that inspires these local experiments and the gamble they entail: banking on the Arab people, trying to reach them again, believing that the only chance of saving—in part, at least—France's position in Algeria is to stake one's all on trust. From the vantage point of Paris, the idea seems mere common sense, the only gamble worth trying. But in Algeria it is quite another kettle of fish, and this must be understood.

If a soldier coming from France shakes hands with an Arab, many French residents of Algiers regard the gesture as impertinent and almost unfriendly to them. This reaction is understandable, for the gesture implies an analysis, even if it is not an explicit one.

It is as though the soldiers were saying: if we're mixed up in this business, it's because the Arabs haven't had a fair deal; if the whole of Algeria is in a state of war now, it's because the Algerian people have built up so much hatred against injustice that their anger has finally exploded in an armed revolt that the people now support and nurture.

It is as though they were thinking: let's forget who's responsible—the Arabs so often blind with passion or the local Frenchmen, so many of whom are exercising their egos. Today the problem is to restore what has been destroyed: the trust that is an indispensable element of life in this communal country, the trust that the soldier from home can win again because he has taken no part in the injustice and has come here without prejudices. This soldier should therefore be an umpire—not exclusively the defender of one side against the other.

Finally, they are saying: look, these Arabs are men, too!

Yes, the gesture is impertinent. It is perhaps naïve, and certainly in the eyes of many French residents of Algeria, particularly those who run the country and manage to "represent" the people, it is a gesture that dangerously fosters revolution.

Most of the residents will assert in good faith that they have an irreplaceable firsthand knowledge of what the Arabs really are, a knowledge which the man from France, in his simplicity, thinks *he* has discovered. They also think that no one can teach them anything, and that they've made every effort—which is probably true—to treat the Arabs kindly. They call it an intellectual's pipe dream, indeed a criminal one, to believe that the revolt was born of a deep-seated popular feeling and that it is spreading today because people are being converted to the cause. The so-called rebellion is the work of a few gangs, founded in the beginning mostly by deserters and criminals, and armed and financed since then by foreign interests—not only Nasser, the most important, but also the Russians, the Tunisians, the Moroccans, even the British and the Americans through their cartels or oil kings.

This is where the dividing-line falls.

If you agree that what is happening is indeed a pan-Islamic plot, engineered by the enemies of France and imposed on the Algerian people by terror—then you are a good man. Your fellow Frenchmen who have lived, worked, and died in this country for several generations can count on you as a friend.

If you stick to the idea that the real roots of the revolt lie in popular resentment, and that the only way of ending it is by treating the people as human beings and seeking contact with them in every possible way—then you are a dreamer, a fellow traveler. You are a threat to the immediate concrete future of the French position in Algeria.

Objectively, both positions are plausible. And therein lies the drama.

The only means of maintaining for a few years more the position of the French residents, *as it is now*, is force. Any other method, if it is to have some chance of founding a durable future for France, will automatically lead to the modification of the *present* forms of colonization, and this transformation will be painful. Very painful for some people; fatal for a few. The facts must be faced.

And the choice they dictate must be made.

An immense army has been sent down to Africa. Is it that army's job to see the transition through by enforcing a certain order on the extremists *on both sides* during the difficult period of change? If so, it will be acting as an umpire, meeting the Arabs when that is necessary and opposing fellow Frenchmen when that is necessary.

Or is the army's sole objective a simpler and more natural one, the protection of the French residents in the social and economic set-up which they have established and for which they exist? Such an attempt is obviously doomed in the long run, and a final explosion is inevitable, but in the meantime it makes sense if there is no shilly-shallying about employing the most effective weapon—terror. Kadar and the Russians will not be in power in Budapest forever; but, for the moment, they are there. However, order through terror, which is what most of the representative French residents in Algeria want, though they don't generally admit it to themselves, is possible only if compromises are ruled out. Otherwise it will be a failure, a useless spilling of blood.

The choice is a political one.

In fact, since the French Premier's capitulation before the mob at Algiers on the terrible day of February 6, the decision has been made. The French Government, incapable of assuming the role of umpire during the transition period, has turned its army into a police force to maintain the *status quo*. Not that this has ever been openly admitted. Which gives rise to a certain disparity between what is said and what is done. Which creates misunderstandings—for example, the Black Commandos.

Working within the framework of order through ruthlessness, attempts like our commando operation are useless and, furthermore, subversive. Even though they may not mean to, they run counter to the purpose of the whole existing system. Naturally, the system defends itself. Here again, feelings are not voiced openly; they are not even admitted; but in practice the authorities must smother an endeavor such as ours. They have no choice.

Naturally, nobody decides to do it. Indeed, no responsible official would condone it if the responsibility were clearly his. Everything happens, though, *as if* a decision had been made to liquidate this dangerous child's play.

Jouve, in his position, was acting sincerely as part of the machinery. A brave and politically minded patriot, he had volunteered for duty in the army of Africa in order to match his actions to his beliefs. Naturally, his political future would not suffer, and he would gain authority in his party's executive, but this was not his fundamental reason. Jouve had wholeheartedly united with his fellow countrymen in angrily decrying on February 6 the threat of a "betrayal" by Paris. And he had decided to join up, to help the French hold on.

Julie, on the other hand, was without doubt a bastard. Had any proof been needed, there was the fact that since his Black Commandos had combed the area from one end to the other, living in the Arabs' pockets, there were actually *even more* crimes than before. This wave of terrorism arose because the rebel command of the area had concentrated forces on the sector in order to prevent the experiment from spreading, to eliminate the establishment of contact.

If we hit back savagely by punishing the people (and, once again, how were we to single out the guilty?) whose confidence we had been courting only yesterday, and if the people returned to their isolation and refused contact on the grounds that it was too risky for them, the *fellagha* would have won the game.

But was the reverse possible? That was what was going to be decided—in our villages, in Algiers, in Paris.

Jouve, like many of his friends who were fighting in the army of Africa—and fighting, usually, with plenty of guts—had remained in close touch with Paris and with all his political friends. Through them he had acquired influential contacts in Algiers: at Headquarters, on the Minister Resident's staff, at the Prefecture, and in those somewhat nondescript circles composed of officials, financiers, newspaper publishers, policemen, big colonists, chairmen of this and that, who exercise the real power and comprise a sort of board of directors of Algeria. The Minister Resident and the prefects are no more than the instruments of this board, which is beginning to penetrate the army—one might almost say, to sink roots there.

On this score again, there has been no question at any moment of a deliberate decision. The phenomenon is a natural one, and that is its strength. Bonds of friendship arise in a hundred different ways. There is the senator who more and more gets the general to listen to his advice, and at the same time there are the grocer's wife who allows the sergeant to enjoy some of the comforts of her home, and the deputy mayor who becomes a friend of the captain commanding the subdistrict. Little by little the blood begins to circulate. Between the old stock of Algeria and the new, fresh from France, a sort of symbiosis develops. The army permits this insistent will of the country's French colony to prevail; no other will, no other *policy* is in the offing, so the army espouses it and tends to become one with it.

Among the most powerful agents of this union, which each week becomes more intimate, are the officers who, like Jouve, have joined the army of Africa because of personal political reasons. Inevitably, they draw others after them; everything conspires toward it.

Sergeant Baral, nicknamed Bunny, came into the guardroom. He was fond of Geronimo and had signed up with him for Jouve's escort group. Baral drew himself to attention and saluted the captain.

Jouve, still dreaming before his battlements, said without paying much attention: "Well, Bunny, anything new?"

"I've just come back from the village, sir. From what I understand, the bastards have knocked off another guy this afternoon."

Jouve looked sharply at the sergeant. "What? And why haven't they told us?"

"I don't know for sure. For one thing, it doesn't throw people any more. It's all in the day's work. And, then, I think the territorials are browned off at us. All this stuff about the Black Commandos—they don't like it. According to what I've heard, they've asked in Algiers to have us replaced by another unit. So they don't let the gendarmes tip us off when there's a new stiff; they prefer to handle things their own way, they say."

Maybe. What the territorials did not know yet was that Jouve had taken over command of the battalion from Julienne, who was completely absorbed in his commando work. Now, they knew Jouve. Before his last leave in Paris he had had dinner several times with the village territorials. They would have confidence in him. And it was urgent that confidence should be restored, because relations between the unit and the local French population had become so strained that there was almost open hostility—which complicated work enormously. Jouve had set himself the task of "buttering up" the French colony by making them feel again that the army was really their own.

And now he had a chance to prove it—his first chance since taking command three days earlier.

He telephoned the gendarmerie immediately and learned that the young French baker in the village had been attacked about three that afternoon. The young man—who had gamely taken over the shop when his father retired to France on the verge of a breakdown—had been murdered at point-blank range: three bullets in the head. His body had not been found until three hours later. The place was a good distance from the village. The population was seething with excitement, and feeling against the battalion was stronger than ever. To them the incident was one more example of how much more interested "these gentlemen"—meaning us —were in sucking up to the gooks than in protecting innocent people, though that was what we were paid for.

Jouve told the gendarmes that he was going there right away, with two of his combat squads.

He sent for Company Sergeant-Major Leroy: his mission was to take five men and advance on the place known as the "Big Olive Tree," where the murder had taken place, from the south. Jouve, with Baral and Geronimo, would come from the north. It was half past six, and they had just an hour left before nightfall. They must lose no time, stay on the alert, and show the apprehensive population that tracking down murderers wasn't going to be a phony any more. Leroy understood. Baral, too.

The technique was simple. Jouve had not needed genius to think of it: it is the oldest of games. In order to reassure the people after a particularly brutal and pointless *fellagha* murder, you've got to produce corpses, if possible. And a reasonable number of them, too. In this case there was, so to speak, some lost time to be made up. Since Espanieul and Julienne had started their experiments in making contact with the Arabs, they had opposed—whenever they could—the customary "gook-hunt" after a murder. They even insisted on an inquiry every time an Arab complained that a patrol had fired at him. The practice had gone so far that Espanieul was openly called the *"fellagha* colonel."

Jouve restored everything to normal. He was certain that he was doing his duty: giving his countrymen needed morale and courage by cowing the rebels with a vigorous retaliation and showing the Arab population—"who only respect force" —that they were in strong hands again.

The total bag when time was up, near the Big Olive Tree, was four "fugitives" brought down by Leroy's patrol and two others by Jouve's. All according to the regulations: a gook is walking in a field, the patrol makes for him and shouts something or other (that is, the "summons to halt"); if he is scared and takes to his heels, the patrol opens fire— "shot while trying to escape." The essential is to be a good shot; if the game is missed, it may try to complain to someone later and give its own version of the incident.

This time there would be no trouble; they had opened fire only when they were sure of themselves. Six bastards in the bag—pretty good. Jouve sent Leroy off in his jeep to tell the territorials before the excitement in the village could turn into an angry riot. The news would calm them down. They would understand that things had changed.

Jouve felt he had made a good beginning at maintaining order: the day was ending well. He gave the Black Angel a great slap on his broad back.

"What d'ya say! I'm not like Julie—I knock 'em dead!"

2/ A *Few Weeks Later*/ Espanieul had spent the whole night trying to calm down—without really succeeding.

He had not found his young wife in the evening in the friendly little Algiers *bistro* where she often had dinner with a few friends; in vain he had dashed through the rooms of the Saint Georges to see if a former Free French comrade had dropped in on the way from Constantine to Oran, as frequently happened. So he had ended by falling back on his favorite sport: racing over the Mitidja roads, after curfew, with all lights on and, at sixty miles an hour, firing at the rabbits caught in the beam of the headlights.

He had spent the night at it, bringing in four hares. His young driver was exhausted, but Espanieul was still raging. Next time he would try for partridges.

Almost as if to give further vent to his spleen, he had called a meeting—and his invitations had been peremptory —for nine in the morning. It was to be in his own room at the farm where he had his headquarters—a way of showing that he meant his position to be respected.

Summoned were the four principal figures of the village of Sidi-Kateb, the administrative center for the southern part of the sector. There were the mayor, whose contacts in Algiers everyone knew of, and his deputy, who had acquired a reputation for being liberal—at least in comparison to his chief. There was the head of the territorials, M. Béjard, a war veteran without much character but with reasonably good intentions. And, finally, there was M. Maroni, one of the big noises among the Mitidja wine-producers. Espanieul had been thinking for at least a fortnight of thrashing things out with them face to face, but something he had heard the day before in the office of an assistant of the Minister at the Government-General had pushed him into action.

Although he had known all his guests individually for

several months, he had never seen them all together, and it seemed to him essential to seize this out-of-the-ordinary opportunity to put the relations between them and him on a new footing. Espanieul never doubted that he would succeed. To tell the truth, he had never even wondered about it. His confidence in his impact on other people, when he chose to make an effort, was limitless.

Julienne and I had also been told to be present, but we did not know exactly why. We were both rather embarrassed, for we guessed that the discussion would probably be about us. As recognition of the Black Commandos had developed, we had become, for different reasons, favorite targets of the right-wing "activists" of Sidi-Kateb.

Espanieul, walking with us to the farm, did not say a word. His black beret askew on his tousled hair, his Colt (taken from one of Rommel's tank crews) on his hip, he strode ahead with his broad shoulders bent.

In front of the house where the party should already have arrived, he hunted in his pockets. "What an idiot I am! The one time they could have been of some use . . . I've forgotten my combat ribbons."

However, Espanieul's ribbons were on the table in his room, arranged with purpose—by the colonel's knowing orderly—in full view of the four civilians who were waiting for us. Ribbons are supposed to be valuable at this sort of meeting; they enable one, Espanieul believed, to dispense with ritual professions of patriotism or belief in the future of France. The display on the table, including the black-and-green ribbon of the Cross of the Liberation and sixteen of the miniature palms that indicate a mention in dispatches, gave a pretty clear idea of how the colonel had spent his time between June 1940 and the fall of Berlin. It was a sight to complete the exasperation of the men across the table, whose proudest moments and happiest memories were tied up with the golden days when North Africa, under Weygand as Governor-General and Marshal Pétain as Head of State in France, had purged itself of such bacillae of decay as trade-unionism and politics.

Espanieul, never a diplomat, had made up his mind that, when dealing with people accustomed to shades of meaning and hints, the one way of trumping a trick was to be frank to the point of rudeness. Having practiced this technique with women and with Ministers alike, without noticing that it seldom came off, he opened fire without any warning.

"Gentlemen, what I have to say to you will be very short, and I don't think there will be any need for me to labor the point or to raise the matter again. You have friends in Algiers, and you count on them to break people you don't like—and to cover for you in your secret deals. Up to now, I'm sure, you've always managed to get away with anything you wanted. But listen to me! I've got contacts, too. I've got my own friends at court, and you may be surprised to hear I've got the lowdown on your dirty schemes. So I give you fair warning: don't try to get rough. This is one time you won't come out on top."

The four visitors were attentive, but they showed no signs of being disturbed. Espanieul's tone was no surprise to them. They knew him, and after one or two attempts to convert him they had come to detest him. What intrigued them now was the strategy that had led him to call this meeting. The colonel, they seemed to insinuate, must have something specific on his mind; just what had he been given the "lowdown" on?

"Well, I learned last night—from a very reliable source, believe me—that your police friends at the Algiers Prefecture have given you the green light to liquidate Captain Julienne, who is here with us. The job would be neatly done, I don't doubt. It isn't *only* the *fellagha* who use hunting

guns and buckshot. . . . Well, listen to me carefully: I'm
not going to go into politics with you. On that score, you
know just where you stand. I believe in a French Algeria
more than you, only I don't believe it can be saved for
France by your methods. We've had that out. If I've convinced you, so much the better. If not, it can't be helped—
we'll save Algeria in spite of you. It'll be a bit harder, but
we'll do it all the same. No, what I want to tell you today
will be much easier to understand. I don't want there to be
any mistake. If the least thing happens to Captain Julienne,
whom you've branded a Communist—it makes things easier,
doesn't it?—but whom I regard as an officer who is a credit to
the French army . . ."

Espanieul stopped a moment, drew his Colt from its
holster (a relic of the American army), put it on the table,
and pointed his finger at his visitors one after another.

"*You—you—you—and you,* I'll take care of you myself, understand? And I won't waste a day or even half a day
carrying out an inquiry, either. I hold you *responsible,* see,
personally responsible for anything that may happen to Julienne. It's up to you to see that nothing does happen to
him."

There was silence.

The mayor had clenched his right fist in his left hand
and was staring straight at Espanieul; he was purple. His
deputy and Béjard, who, as lesser figures, did not feel themselves in the front line, were staring at their feet. M. Maroni
easily dominated the situation. His hands on the crook of his
stick, his head leaning against the wall behind his chair, his
eyes narrowed almost to slits, he took in the shabby room
and the colonel and the whole scene with an air of lofty indifference. He was not amused.

For more than twenty years, since he had succeeded
his dead father at the head of the huge Karmeur estates,

which had grown even bigger since the last war, Maroni had seen a series of gesticulating figures come over from France, determined to change everything in Algeria. Their plans had been naïve or hasty; they had not realized the real relationship of the forces opposed to each other, and in the final analysis they had meant nothing. He could barely remember their names: captains, prefects, governors, generals, civil-service inspectors, priests (these last the most dangerous of all), a whole string of supposedly important people who had passed across Algeria and left hardly a trace. Yet what had he and his colleagues had to use in opposing such intruders?

What had they had at the time of De Gaulle and of the successive Governors-General—Chataigneau, Naegelen, and only yesterday Soustelle? Money, naturally, but only the most elementary sort of Communist propaganda dares assert that the representatives of the State are bought over the counter. The newspapers—yes, that was another matter. The Algerian press bewitches, inveigles, and intimidates its victims and succeeds in fabricating an ephemeral world in which ideas and convictions are distorted and dissolved and give place to an unfamiliar giddiness—a subtle brain-washing in which the reader is finally victimized.

What else had they had then? Very little indeed. Think of it, they had not even the doltish atrocities of the *fellagha* which were so valuable to the Maronis of Algeria today. There had been no *fellagha* then. If one of those imported straw bosses had looked for a moment behind the stage set, he would have realized the extent of his power. Fortunately, it is the nature of such stooges to accept the world of appearances and to perform within the make-believe walls. . . .

And now this little colonel was taking his part seriously and wanting to stick his squirt-gun into the stage windows and the paper curtains. Too late! Those aren't theatrical properties any more, my friend, they're hard realities, and you'll break your toy pistol on them and your head with it if you push things too far. Today the Maronis of North Africa can count on a good deal more than two or three million pounds and two or three newspapers to keep their Algeria. They've got *power*, the real thing, the power of Paris, delivered on their doorstep. They have the French Parliament, the French Government, the French Budget, and the French army—isn't that enough for you? And, of course, I was forgetting the finishing touch: the brutality of the *fellagha*, the key factor that locks the whole system together—the cover of the pot. Will it blow up? Perhaps. But how long will that take? The *status quo* may hold out. And, anyway, to smash it will need more than a little colonel commanding a little sector. . . . The icy gaze of Maroni's half-closed eyes remained fixed on Espanieul.

The commander of the territorials, who felt as embarrassed as anyone, took it upon himself to make a reply. "It seems to me, colonel, that you think you're dealing with a handful of buck sergeants. Your manner of speaking—"

"Please, Béjard!" Maroni interrupted. "There's nothing more to be said. You don't imagine we're going to stoop to any discussion with this gentleman. . . ."

And M. Maroni, having made his feelings clear, turned scornfully from Espanieul. The three others rose, too, and they disappeared together.

Julienne did not start talking at once. He began to pace slowly up and down the room with his big head bowed. His manner suggested an aging wild boar a little tired of jungle fighting. Espanieul had relaxed and was sitting down at last, flicking a few specks of dust off the shining barrel of his Colt. The fatigue of the night had obviously been dispelled by the satisfaction he had derived from his little expression of opinion.

"Surely you realize, sir, that Maroni and his friend the

mayor are about ten times stronger than we?" Julienne said in a very calm, almost indifferent tone.

"You're wrong, my friend, you're wrong," Espanieul answered. "Maybe they are ten times stronger, as you say, but in *their* system. If I let myself be caught in that, I'm done for. If I try to beat them at the little game of pulling wires at Algiers, I agree that I've had it. That's just what I won't do. I steer clear of the system. Take it from me, they're the ones who don't know what to do next; they're not among gentlemen any more. If I don't subscribe to the rules, they just can't play. There are certain things one isn't supposed to say. Well, I'm saying them, and I'm going to shout them from the housetops now. I'm going to say that these gentlemen are sabotaging us, and that they've got their strong-arm men, not just to rub out Arabs they don't like, but any Frenchman who sticks his nose into their little affairs. I'm going to say that pacification's possible only if we start by getting rid of these boys *first*. As long as they run this country, the *fellagha* will be cocks of the walk and people will be standing in line at rebel recruiting depots. What we want to know is: are we here to protect the pile Maroni's made for himself and to keep that other fat slob's behind in the mayoral chair, or are we here to save Algeria—because they're not at all the same thing."

"I agree. . . . The answer is: to defend Maroni."

"Not me!"

"Then you're *really* asking for it. The system's stronger than you. Don't have any doubts about that."

"Wrong again, Julienne. Probably the system is capable of kicking me out of Algeria. But you're forgetting that I'm capable of kicking up a hell of a stink myself and blowing the roof off what goes on here. I'll bet you that will interest a few guys back home. They won't feel inclined to laugh it off when they hear from someone fresh from Algeria that pacification's nothing but eyewash, that nobody gives a damn about it—except the bill-posters—and that if anyone here takes the official speeches seriously and gets it into his head to win the Arab population back by taking care of them, listening to what they're saying, talking to them, and trusting them, he's labeled a crackpot and sent home with a report plastered to his backside explaining that he's next door to being a Communist. Oh, no! Take it from me, this enormous swindle may seem natural to you because you live in it, but seen from Paris it's something else again."

"On the contrary, it's just the same. The longer the deal lasts, the more comfortable the Paris crowd feels." Julienne was still pacing heavily between the low, bare walls of the room. He was too fond of Espanieul not to be moved by his beliefs, fond enough to say what he felt. "I admire your ideals, but I don't share your illusions. Because you're honest and take a look at things for yourself, you discover that the Arabs are wretched and—only too often—treated like cattle. You're a hundred per cent against injustice and falsehood, and you're certain that when you denounce the bastards who oppose you and have the guts to fight them, you're serving the general interest. You think that's the meaning of pacification. That's great. But who are you going to convert? Not the people whose whole position depends on the perpetuation of injustice—not Maroni. Not the people who've become Maroni's accomplices because they've given up fighting against him—not the Government. Not the people who've been committed for months now to the policy of repression, and therefore to all the lies, and who'd have to eat their own words if they admitted that what you're saying is true—not the French body politic . . ."

"What the hell are you doing in the Black Commandos, then?" Espanieul demanded. "You're wasting your time!"

"I probably am, if I thought twice about it—so I don't

think about it. And while I'm in this mess I can feel at least that I'm in a real world, that I'm touching with my two hands and my whole body a reality that nobody officially will admit exists. When I go to sleep in a dark little room in a *mechta* with Omar or Selma or Mansour—who's become a friend and who's talked freely to me—and with my three or four lads from Toulon or Montpellier who've come to feel at home with the gooks and talk to them like human beings— well, I feel good. It doesn't go any further than that. I've stopped thinking for a moment that I'm going to revolution- ize the war in Algeria. It's the other way around now—I know it's going to break me. Meanwhile, I'm still a man, and a very presumptuous one, as you see, but with no sort of am- bition."

Espanieul always enjoyed listening to Julienne, up to a certain point. To lead an idealistic life seemed to him the thinnest of satisfactions. He was out for efficiency, action, results—and with no sort of modesty. Now that he was con- vinced that the whole system ought to be blown sky high, he had no doubt about his ability to do the job.

However, first things first.

"Listen, old buddy, you're off the beam. Don't forget the reason I sent for Maroni and his brown-nosers wasn't to change French history, but something much simpler: to prevent your getting knocked off within a week. Don't think their little plan wasn't all set. My pal at the GG knows these characters. He didn't send for me for the hell of it. He was risking his job by doing it. But, after today, you can take it from me, they won't try anything for a long time. At least we won a breathing-space. What comes later is any- body's guess."

Espanieul had instinctively chosen to fight as soon as he had seen the first signs of a showdown.

The progress of the Black Commando experiment—like other attempts of the same kind—had become a bugbear for the established order, so the sabotage had started. The wrecking was not deliberate or even conscious, but natural reflex action.

It was a little difficult to start a frontal attack on Galland and Espanieul—particularly Galland. The machine had therefore set out to win him over, to rope him in. He was invited to Algiers, where he was let into secrets and treated as an insider. One of the outstanding generals of the army of Algeria asked Colonel Galland to a quiet little dinner party, with only two other friends, who were equally influential. They asked Galland to join their brilliant backstage group of officers who knew what they wanted, and whose ultimate objective was to rid themselves, when the time came, of the poor civilians who were flapping about at the Government-General and to set up a military government capable of keeping a firm grip on Algeria. Galland pretended not to understand.

He returned that night pretty depressed. He did not feel like being alone, so in the middle of the night he dropped in on us at our mountain hut to unload some of his despondency. What was left now? Although we had long realized the nullity of the civil administration, we could no longer ignore the respected military leaders, the brilliant soldiers, who had let their heads be turned so far that they imagined that the only problem in Algeria was to know how to use force and thought they could replace the anemic civilian Government and restore France to what they called her greatness. The realization bewildered Galland. It was not in his nature to throw in the sponge, so little by little he threw himself into his daily work again, but for the first time the futility of it had him tied up in knots.

Because of his appearance, Espanieul inspired little fear

in the people who mattered. He was generally regarded as flighty and ready to dash off in whatever direction one wanted to lead him. This illusion was to his advantage—it gave him a handicap over his opponent. As a result, he was no more than a purely local target, for his opponents believed that it would be easy to turn him around whenever it became necessary.

So, to liquidate the Black Commandos, the machine had started to work first on Julienne and then on me.

On his last trip to Paris, Espanieul had been called in by the Minister, who opened the interview by thrusting a report under Espanieul's nose with a curt: "What do you say to that?"

Espanieul was stupefied to discover that the Minister had personally received, from two different sources, and was gravely considering what he called a "report" on the activities of J.J.S.S. while using the Black Commandos as a cover. What was it all about?

As one of my commando squad I had taken a young corporal who, though he'd had a slight brush with the law at Clichy and was the godson of a Paris scholar with a lot of influence in the extreme right-wing political militias, was quickly accepted by my squad. Young Franchi did his commando work well, and he had endless conversations with the Arabs, which seemed to please him a lot.

One evening Captain Jouve, after a chat with his friends of the Algiers Prefecture, had gone to Franchi and asked him, as a patriotic duty, to draw up a report on "the way in which J.J.S.S., under the pretext of nomad work with the Arabs, was paving the way for negotiations with the FLN."

Franchi had performed his duty. He had got quite excited about his little fairy-tale as he went along, achieving a fine peak of indignation as he recounted my betrayal of my duties as an officer.

Here is a sample of his fiction: "We were with some influential F.L.N. figures in a mountain *mechta* when J.J.S.S., who felt he was safe, showed his hand and said: 'Gentlemen, I invite you to Paris, to come and negotiate with my political friends—all the expenses of the trip will be on me, naturally.' And the lot of us, including myself, so as not to arouse suspicion, opened a bottle of champagne and drank to the future of Algeria. I was revolted at such a piece of treason on the part of an officer, and I made up my mind to go on following him so as to be able to denounce his activities." (I quote from memory.)

The marvelous "Franchi report," which had been typed out in six copies thanks to Captain Jouve, had been given to certain police officials in Algiers and sent off at the same time to Franchi's right-wing godfather. Thus it reached the Minister, who apparently neither doubted its contents for a moment nor felt the least need to check on its authenticity. Swallowing it whole, he had sent for Espanieul—not to question him, but to insist that he put an end to "this treason" of the Black Commandos.

Espanieul had long since ceased to be impressed by Ministers. With characteristic bluntness he put matters in their proper perspective and expressed astonishment that a man responsible for so many important decisions (which were turning out so badly, too) should have time for such obvious nonsense as this "report." How had he been able to take this absurdity seriously for even half a second?

But that was not the real question, and Espanieul felt it in his bones: the job of wrecking was under way.

Suddenly he saw how the right-wing "National Volunteers," the cops, the hangers-on from the colonial period, the criminals safely camouflaged by their uniforms, Maroni's millions, the inadequacy of the Ministers, and the general indifference were forming a curious network around a common idea: the necessity for the war. And how a swarm of different kinds of men, tied up with the war or living on it, were instinctively reacting, often unaware but always in the same direction: promoting the conditions that would permit the war to go on.

Espanieul had come back to Algeria determined to fight body and soul against the machine and against the web of hidden force. His method of deduction was to dash into action and then react to the consequences. He had thrown himself into the Black Commandos, instinctively certain that if this venture could arouse the hostility of such a formidable coalition, its idea must be a sound one—and that, the more violent the collision, the more clearly would the idea emerge. Confidently, Espanieul waited for the venture to be recognized for what it was.

The system's second attack had been launched immediately afterward.

One morning Espanieul had received in his official mail one of the little colored slips, famous throughout the army, that intimate, always in the curtest terms, that an officer is "on the files" of Military Security, or MS. There is never any explanation, only the slip. The officer named thereon is under suspicion and is not to be trusted with confidential missions or responsible commands. The slip on Espanieul's desk bore the name of Captain Julienne.

For nearly fifteen years Espanieul had looked on Julienne as the most straightforward, reliable, and human person he knew; he had trusted him as he did no one else. Except for Galland, he was the only man for whom Espanieul would have answered as he would for himself. Because of this trust he had put Julienne in charge of the Black Commandos.

With Julienne so unjustly on the files at MS, Espanieul launched an impossible one-man offensive against Military

Security, and, oddly enough, his unorthodox siege was not entirely fruitless. Galland had received—because people were beginning to be wary of Espanieul—a personal letter from the Minister's Chief of Staff. It said that Lieutenant-Colonel Espanieul would be well advised not to press the matter, "since Captain Julienne must be regarded, on the basis of detailed information, as a *dangerous extremist*." In the MS vocabulary, this was a euphemism for *Communist agent*.

With the help of Galland, who seemed appalled at such idiocy, Espanieul had managed to trace the defamation of Julienne back to its source. It had begun with a recent incident. On a public-works job under army control, the native and European workers had joined to call a strike, and consequently had been fired by the director. The European shop foreman had then started negotiations with the management, recommending that, under certain conditions, only the Moslem workers should be dismissed. Julienne, who was in the sector, had intervened in the most violent terms, telling both the management and the foreman that they were "the lowest kind of bastards, saboteurs of Algeria, cowards," and so on.

The trade-union representative, furious at being accused of selling out his pals, had hoped at least to get his own job back by sending to Paris a "report" on Julienne which denounced him, by and large, as a secret agent of the Communist Party. This was just what Military Security, the heads of the General Staff, and the Minister had needed, and in short order there appeared in Espanieul's mail the little colored slip, from which there was no appeal.

The circle was closing in. The latest alarm indicated that Julienne's very life was at stake. And the calm and curiously confident attitude of Maroni in the face of Espanieul's threat increased the colonel's feeling that he was in the heart of a malevolent jungle. He began to be conscious of a fear that he might lose, not so much his life, but his honor and his ideals—that he might be crushed by the invisible, omnipresent machine which has all Algeria in its grip. This apprehension, plus his discovery of the nature of the war, drove him to the only moral refuge, the only help he could think of: Galland.

3/ Colonel Galland had left his HQ in the plains and had gone up with an escort of three men for an inspection taking place in the mountains above Ouled Smar, to the west. This area, about which we knew little, was his favorite spot. The fact that we had not seen much of him in our sector for nearly three weeks was probably due to the attraction Ouled Smar had for him.

At the time when we were starting our first Black Commandos (on Galland's inspiration), a similar experiment was being put into effect in the west. There, too, the object was to restore contact with the Moslems, and it centered on a program of local projects (building, irrigation, farmers' cooperatives) and medical services.

The wretchedness of the people in this area is almost unbelievable. Some of the *mechtas* are sickening to see. Most of the adults have lost the sight of at least one eye because of a kind of ophthalmia which turns the eyeball into a whitish protruding globe, while many of the children have lost all their hair and their heads are covered with green moss, dotted with scabs, which is eating into the scalp. When our young soldiers went into these *mechtas*, they felt nauseated for the rest of the day. There was no question of asking them to go and eat and sleep there, as we did in our area. Galland had launched another scheme: he saw to it that the able-bodied Arabs left and found work; meanwhile, medical-aid posts were established between the *douars*.

The venture was probably even more chancy and tenuous than that of the commandos. Naturally, the only people Galland could call on to supervise the various jobs, to look after and if possible cure the sick, were callow soldiers who understandably preferred to be sent out "on an operation" scaring up the *fellagha*. To turn an entire military system against its nature, by converting it into an instrument of permeation and pacification, takes iron will, scrupulous daily supervision, and tireless missionary zeal. And additional fervor was required in this instance because the *fellagha*, for fear of being destroyed by the success of our contact with the population, were now counterattacking for all they were worth. They chose as victims those of our men who stood out most for their selfless work with the Arabs or those Moslems who were most willing to work with us. In both cases, the objective was the same: to exasperate our troops, to provoke reprisals, to cut short the experiment, and to break off the contact. So far they had not succeeded. Galland was holding on.

When we went over to see him that day, we felt we were going to our fountainhead. To share in his freshness of outlook, to draw from the success of his work the encouragement we needed to persist with our own seemed to us, as we left our poisoned atmosphere, a cure we simply could not do without.

We found Colonel Galland in the midst of a little improvised camp sitting in his command jeep, surrounded by a group of trucks that had brought some detachments of our unit from the village of Ouled Smar to the top of the road. He was writing.

The curt greetings of his officers and the tension we discerned in his face when he looked up made us feel immediately that we had not chosen a good day. But Galland was always courteous.

"Hello, Espanieul, how are things with you?"

"Bad, sir. We need you. . . . We're putting up all the fight we can, but we don't carry the guns. The pressure's enormous, everything's giving way. I feel as if I were caught in a wringer."

Galland, who usually was so attentive and took such pains to listen and to understand, was clearly thinking of something else, wrapped up in his own affairs. He looked down again at his papers and scribbled an addition or two to the text he was going over.

"Look here," he said, "we'll talk about it later, if you want to. At the moment, I'm awfully sorry, but I've got to think about this business here first. As a matter of fact, you can help me. It's not funny, I can assure you. If you feel caught, then where am I? . . . Why don't you begin by reading the report I've just done for Headquarters?"

He passed us the sheets of paper on which he had recorded, in his plain, unvarnished style, the most recent—it had happened the day before—of the incidents that were steadily sabotaging his work.

The Ouled Smar business was nothing unusual, no more serious than others. But, probably because of our own difficulties and perhaps also because Galland himself was beginning to question his outlook, we became at that moment fully aware of the extent of the French tragedy in Algeria. The name of Ouled Smar, therefore, more than any other, will always remain inextricably bound up with our own venture, and the commonplace affair that took place there is still, even today, a symbol for us of the pitiless grinding of the wheels.

Here are the essential passages in Colonel Galland's report to Army Headquarters in Algiers, which was later transmitted, with others of the same kind, to the civil authorities.

Report to Headquarters

Subject: *Consequences of an operation in the Ouled Smar area.*

I have the honor of confirming and elaborating the oral report made this morning.

The officer commanding the subdistrict of Ouled Smar, Lieutenant Rainier, was notified during the night of Sunday 13th to Monday 14th by the usual radio message that the troops in the adjacent sector were taking part in a combined operation with artillery support and air cover and might have occasion, as the encirclements materialized, to pursue their action in this sector.

Having already observed the consequences of these operations and the losses they inevitably occasion among the local population, with whom we are trying to develop contacts, Lieutenant Rainier, in a message of acknowledgment, made his usual request. He asked that the officers on the operation take great pains to avoid any form of violence against the inhabitants of the area, most of whom are employed on our construction projects.

On Monday morning, troops were in fact seen in action on the heights to the north of the subdistrict. . . .

Toward the end of the afternoon, a Moslem of the douar of Djebabra came to see Lieutenant Rainier and reported to him that two of the sons of the family next door had been killed by our troops and that some ten other inhabitants had been made prisoners.

Lieutenant Rainier proceeded to Djebabra. He personally identified the two bodies. The parents of the two young people had been beaten, their mechta had been sacked, and, according to them, a sum of 100,000 francs, accruing from the sale of the douar crops in the town market, had been taken off one of their sons.

On the way back to Ouled Smar, Lieutenant Rainier was informed by other inhabitants, who had come to meet him on the road, that eight more corpses had been found in a ditch near another group of mechtas.

He proceeded there himself and identified the bodies: they were those of workers employed on one of our projects.

The victims were known throughout the area, and the feeling aroused is considerable. An additional detail, which also spread quickly, added to the confusion. When the inhabitants showed their identity cards—made out by us to prevent local workers from being held as suspects in an ordinary shakedown—to the troops engaged in the operation, the soldiers confiscated the cards and, in certain instances, tore them up on the spot.

It is probably unnecessary to emphasize to Headquarters the consequences of this kind of operation on the work of pacification which we are trying to pursue in this area. The present report follows on earlier communications.

A SP. 82,719

SIGNED: *Colonel Galland*

CO NORTHERN OS

"They'll get us in the end, no doubt about it," said Galland. "But I'll fight on as long as there's a hope left. And to the very end I'll give them the facts. That's the only way of putting their responsibilities in front of them—the only hope of making them realize what they're doing."

"Do you still hope for that?"

"Here? Probably not. They're completely mad. They don't see any more. In Paris, maybe. The advantage of a written report is that it gets to Paris. Probably very few people worry about it, but there's bound to be someone who'll ask himself questions. And, let's face it, that's all I can do. I'm not a politician, I'm a soldier. I can put down the facts and forward all pertinent papers through the regular channels. For the moment, that's all. But, wait. If the system which we are witnessing and which manages every day, here or somewhere else, to demolish chances of building something solid in Algeria—if it goes on revolving and nothing happens, then not only pacification will be at stake, but far greater problems as well. First of all, that of the army as a whole . . ."

It was far more than the commandos, or the construction projects, or Algeria, or even the army which was getting Galland down. This extraordinarily forthright man seemed to us to be shaken in his underlying confidence in France itself. In Galland's distress, better controlled and more eloquent, we all recognized the echo of our own, which we sometimes managed to forget.

The patrols were coming back one after another, making oral reports to Galland's officers and wandering off over the bank into the grass or dashing off in vehicles. A persistent breeze began to stir, a gentle reminder that evening was at hand. Espanieul was rereading the conclusion of the brief report. He lifted his green eyes, full of sadness now, to Galland.

"What do you think they'll do when they get this paper?"

"Order an inquiry, as usual. When a so-called blot appears on the record—one that may show up too much—they try to gain time first: they call for a 'report.' When the report is a little too strong, they decide, in a relaxed way, of course, to open an 'inquiry'—that'll take plenty of time. When there have been several inquiries and all of them have confirmed the facts, there are still other devices to resort to. A 'commission of inquiry,' for example, whose job is to inquire into the inquiries and to 'recommend' measures. By that time . . ."

Galland took out a cigarette, and lighted it slowly, playing with the match to dispel his impatience.

The patrols were all back now. One by one, the officers in charge came and asked Galland's permission for their men to go back to their quarters.

"They refuse to see that what's wrong isn't a series of 'cases' but the whole system. They get very indignant about 'abuses,' 'extortions,' and 'deplorable incidents'—as if they were *exceptions*. The exception is just the opposite. The exceptions are people like us here, like Carlin in the Constantine area, like Ventura in the north, like a few others—people who are still trying to talk to the Arabs. But the torches those men carry are being extinguished, one by one. Because a war is being waged here, and the army's in for a long siege. And anyone who tries to put a spoke in the wheels of this endless war becomes a suspect, whether he's a *curé* or a captain."

"Why do you expect them to question the system when they are the system?" Espanieul asked. "You can't ask people to condemn themselves. Even if they were saints—"

But Galland interrupted. "Excuse me, the only policy I've got is that laid down by the Government, which I'm serving. I don't ask for any other. I simply ask them to make up their minds to apply it. 'Pacification,' the Government's written directives, the official proclamations—I'm all for them. It shouldn't be impossible to get back to all that, since that's the policy—I repeat, the very policy they've chosen and proclaimed."

Julienne, who by nature was not so trustful as Galland,

had for some weeks now given up thinking about the over-all problems and was trying to find contentment in just doing his job. But Galland was a big man, one of the foremost in the army.

We were alone now except for Galland's waiting escort, and the silence had closed in on us. Against the impressive background of the *jebel* under the clear sky of a winter's night, Julienne found once more, with an access of hope, the freshness of a younger spirit and the strength to size up the enormous obstacles he had given up facing.

"If you're going to take that line, sir," he said, "you're going to run into something much bigger than the second-rateness of a Minister, the vanity of a general, or the stupidity of a patrol commander. You're going to find yourself up against the real reason for the contradictions you're attacking. If the talk is of 'pacification' and the fact is the practice of terrorist methods, that's no accident. It had to be that way, considering the forces pitted against each other. M. Maroni and M. Lacoste, for instance, didn't constitute a fair match. Maroni had won in advance, and Lacoste *depends* on him. Lacoste can go on laying down all the policies in the world, on paper. But he's part of the system of which the Maronis are the very center; he exists only by their permission. So he makes war to maintain their established order—as long as possible. Hence your failures, and ours, and the others. And today's twelve corpses, not to speak of tomorrow's."

"I'd believe that," Galland said, "if I really thought that your M. Maroni and the people who run this country with him were blind enough to choose a few poor years of respite, maybe even a few months, before the inevitable explosion, rather than cut their losses and try to save the future. They don't give me the impression of being that stupid."

·

"In that case, Mussolini had only to stay a Social-Democrat and Hitler wouldn't have started the war—it would all have been so much more reasonable."

Picking up an olive branch, Galland began to draw little squares on the ground—which was already a little wet with dew—as he always did when he was thinking. "According to you, the idea of pacification, of a reconciliation in this country—of a future for France, in short—is a myth, and this vicious circle of brutality is inevitable?"

"The political situation in France being what it is, I should say: on the whole, yes. Mind you, *political* isn't quite the right word. People immediately take it to mean *parliamentary*. Well, I don't care a damn whether M. Lacoste or M. Thingumabob is in Algiers or whether the present Government stays in power or not—it's all the same. I'm talking about the French set-up as a whole. The nature of the ruling class, the pattern of the big interests, the leadership of the masses, the news—in a business as vital for the country as this war has become, it's all those things that lie behind the real major decisions. I don't need to tell you that what goes on here is anything but the result of a Minister's ideas—or of a Government's. . . ."

Galland got up, and beckoned to his escort to get ready to leave. We shook ourselves, too, trying to dissipate the inner chill.

Galland turned to Julienne: "Maybe we are on the eve of one of those occasions when, as you say, the whole form of the nation's life is in the melting-pot. I felt that a hundred per cent once—in '40. What I feel today, Julienne, is a little different. As if what we were going to see soon wouldn't be another '40 but, in a way, the agonizing moment when the challenge that one man issued then was going to receive, nearly twenty years later, the answer of France."

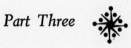

Part Three

AMONG THE FRENCH

Chapter One

1/ Now that I had seen the summer, autumn, and winter pass, I believed that I had penetrated to the very heart of the war and understood all its many aspects. I never thought that a startling short cut, taken quite by chance, just in one day would show me yet one more facet and thus give a new dimension to the tragedy.

Lieutenant Colonel Espanieul was on a mission at Constantine with a general of the eastern theaters of operations. Major Henry, his second-in-command, had taken over the regiment. Breakfast in the old garage with Henry was a charming interlude. Like so many people who have been through several campaigns in Indochina, he suffered from liver trouble, and he dreaded the beginning of the day's worries. His way of trying to prolong the carefree night was to reminisce or tell long stories, full of poetic touches, which kept the door closed a few minutes more on hard reality.

But reality asserted itself, just the same, in the person of Lieutenant Martin, who was at the opposite pole from the world of dreams.

"Hiya, boys! Got a cup of coffee for an old soldier?" he said. He picked up a chair and sat down beside us.

Martin was not often with us. He was commanding a battalion in a neighboring sector and came over, from time to time, only to get the lowdown on our difficulties and to tell us about his. On the surface, his huge frame still emanated joviality and high spirits; if you looked more deeply, however, you saw that the war in Algeria had got under his skin. Martin had changed a lot. His self-assurance of last August, his calm certainty that he had everything taped ("the *fellagha* are just Viets". . . "it's all a Moscow plot"), had apparently not survived his day-by-day experiences. He had discovered for himself the appalling vacuum in which the army was floundering, the depressing absence of any meaningful plan of action, the inevitable deterioration of our men's morale and behavior. And what we had heard recently of Martin's doings had made a big impression on us—particularly on Henry, who had known him so long. Henry lost no time in questioning him.

"Well, Martin, those contacts of yours with the FLN, are they getting you anywhere?"

The last time I had seen Martin—about six weeks before —stood out in my memory.

It had been about six in the morning, and, with winter coming on, it was still dark. With the aid of a flashlight, I had searched an old unfamiliar farm looking for Martin's room in order to introduce him to a writer from Paris who had been visiting Espanieul's HQ and was leaving by the eight-o'clock plane from Maison Blanche. I did not want him to leave our area without adding to his collection of impressions a few moments with this off-beat character. Martin, as a sergeant with the *maquis* in Vietnam, used to get mimeographed lessons from a Paris correspondence school; while he was picking up spelling from his simplified grammars, he learned the theory of war from the essays of Mao Tse-tung. Moreover, distrusting everything he had not thought of or rediscovered for himself, he developed a fiercely independent mind, and his freshness of approach gave added color to each aspect of the outside world which he encountered.

We found Martin's huge body, naked and hairy, flopped on an army cot. He woke up and reached for a khaki bath towel—one of the practical horrors of the American surplus stocks—using it as a loincloth. With a kindliness that had an odd touch of melancholy he led us out into the little farmyard. For a long time now he had been accustomed to sleep naked in the cool autumnal nights in the *jebel,* just as he had formerly done in the dank warmth of the jungle. He couldn't wait to tell us his story.

"I've failed," he told us abruptly. "Last night I rounded up all my young second lieutenants in command of our little posts in the mountains." He turned to the writer. "Look, this'll interest you, coming from Paris; this is one of the things that never enter your heads up there. The second lieutenant, you see, is the foundation of everything here; he represents the smallest independent center of responsibility. If the lieutenants take an interest in this war, if they're alive and full of guts and put their hearts into the job, things'll work out. But if they don't give a damn, if all they think about is how to mark time till they're demobbed, everything goes to the dogs. . . . Well, as soon as I got to this unit, I could see things weren't going right; the morale just wasn't what it ought to be. And yet there's a nice enough bunch of kids here—twenty-four, twenty-six, about that age. Two or three of them have been through Central Tech, there are a few teachers, a subprefect, and there's even one who's running his own factory near Pau—one ought to be able to do something with them. That's what I thought."

Martin picked a long stalk from the grass in the farmyard. He liked to tickle his chin while he talked—it helped.

"So yesterday I asked them all to dinner with me at HQ. They all came down from the mountains. I gave them a little talk just to tell them how they could do their job and train their men and get out of the rut, get rid of the couldn't-care-less line of thinking, and then I told them to ask me questions. We went on talking till two in the morning. . . . Well, I've had it! Oh, yes, I could read their minds; they went away just as skeptical as ever. I didn't get to first base. I'll have to say it all again, three, four, a dozen times to make a dent.

You'd think they were steel-plated. With some it's probably just a plain overdose of ego. Others have made up their minds not to 'fall for all that.' Believe me, none of them give a damn!"

He threw away his grass stalk and rubbed his hands briskly. "God damn, I'm sure glad you dropped in to see me! You couldn't have picked a better time. I wasn't looking forward to waking up this morning. I was beat when I went to bed."

The pale, cold light of dawn, the few wisps of mist in the air, gave to the cracked walls of the farm and the little woods beyond them the look of a stage set. A moment later we felt we really were in the theater, for suddenly there appeared before us, as if he had emerged from the wings to declaim a monologue on man's sad estate, a sort of ghost in battle dress. Dragging a long rifle, his face blurred by fatigue, he moved with steps so slow and muffled that not one of us had heard him coming. It was a second lieutenant of Martin's unit returning from a night patrol. But—alone?

Martin hardly turned a hair. He seemed to take the man's presence for granted as a perfect, living example of what he had just been telling us, and he addressed the apparition in a tone of affectionate pity:

"Well, Picot, old man—no one with you?"

The young lieutenant, pulling himself together with an effort, managed a salute and replied with so much lassitude and distress that the tone of his voice seemed to sum up in that single moment the bewildered solitude of an entire generation—his own and his comrades', betrayed by a world where there was no truth.

"No one, sir. I called for volunteers last night when I got back. Not one. I tried to explain to them what you'd told us. But no one understood. So I went out all the same. I thought perhaps that'd make them feel small."

Picot saluted again and disappeared in the direction of the kitchen.

"My solitary success," Martin said with a gentle smile on his big face.

Our visitor had taken leave of Martin on this tableau, almost too dramatic to be true. . . .

It was just after this that Martin, in an attempt to break out of the vicious circle of terrorism and reprisals, had asked the command for authorization to try to make contact with the local rebel leaders. That was all we knew. We were waiting eagerly to know the results of his venture.

Martin unbuckled his belt, put his gun down on the mess table, and cut himself a slice of the field bakery's bread.

"I'd told myself: there's no way out—for us or for them. We have our foul-ups when things get all screwed up, but so do they. I got some dope on the chief in my sector: he's got all he can handle with a bunch of kids under his command who pull crazy tricks, kill and steal to beat hell, and pile it on so thick that he's even had to liquidate one or two to maintain his authority. So, according to our information, he's probably not one of the extremists. That's about all I could get on him, except his name, Ramdane—I didn't even know where he came from or whether he spoke French. I thought: anyway, we could get together and I could explain that he's getting nowhere because we'll always be stronger than him, and tell him that if he was willing to give a fair trial to an experiment in the area, I could take charge of liquidating the local toughs who go in for private counter-terrorism and I could kick out the dumbest of the mayors and the territorials, and try to change things a bit here, all inside a French set-up, of course. Why not?"

So while we were congratulating ourselves on the audacity of our Black Commando experiments and drawing down the thunderbolts of the system on our heads, Martin had pushed the argument to its logical conclusion and sought out the FLN itself. We stared at him with considerable admiration as he gulped down a second cup of coffee.

"No dice," Martin went on. "I saw the guy, of course. Twice, in fact. But it's finished. The two of us discovered at just about the same time that we're hamstrung. He got rapped over the knuckles by his people, and Algiers gave it to me good—below the belt, too. While a top-priority order to break off all contacts was on its way to me from Algiers, I got a letter from him by a roundabout way. Somebody else had drafted it and written it for him, obviously. It was on official paper, with the letterhead 'Army of National Liberation—Headquarters,' and it notified me, in a propaganda tone, that we couldn't meet again 'on the unofficial basis of our previous interviews.' Hell, it's not worth the effort, it can't get you anywhere. So we start our damn-fool 'operations' again, and he goes on with his butchery."

"What's he like, this Ramdane?"

"Well, he was kind of interesting. I wasn't expecting a type like that. He asks me, see, through our undercover go-between, to come to the meeting place—about twelve miles from my farm, in the mountains, on the side of the road—and I have to be alone and unarmed. I agree so that he'll trust me, and I start off at nightfall in a Citroën. When I arrive at the place, I get out and wait. In about five minutes two guys come out of the woods. One's very young and looks dumb, a hefty type with dark skin. The other one's dark, too, but thin and intelligent-looking, quite gentlemanly, really, with two cotton rank-badges on the shoulder straps of his jacket. He turns out to be Ramdane. Both of them are wearing American battle dress, like us. Ramdane hasn't got anything but a cane in his hands, but there's an automatic in his belt. His bodyguard's carrying a tommy-gun. They never believed, see, that I would really come unarmed. Well, they come up, Ramdane introduces himself, and the conversation starts. Ramdane talks as good French as we do—he told me he'd been at Algiers University till he took to the *maquis* last year. What impresses me most about the way he looks is his shoes. They've got a shine on them like a looking-glass. And his hands are clean, and his nails are as well-trimmed as if he's just come from a manicurist. Started me thinking about the people the *maquis* are recruiting. . . . Oh, well, it's all washed up. All that trouble for nothing!"

I had only a few minutes left before my appointment in the village, so I had to say good-by to Martin. As I got up, I remembered our last meeting.

"Your team of young second lieutenants, how's that going?"

Martin made a gesture with his big right hand, which still held the coffee cup, and, screwing up his eyes, said in the tone in which he would have said "Forget it":

"Oh, that's going all right. They've been sensible and settled down some. Good kids, you know. And then they're being demobbed a month from now. That helps."

Martin, too, had seen a good deal of the war. Like us, he had rammed his head against a lot of stone walls. Every time he had explored what looked like a way out, he had found himself headed toward the inevitable end. This dead end, which blocked each successive attempt at a piecemeal solution, was the absence at the top of any guidance, of any co-ordinated—which means political—outlook that would give a chance to the individual efforts and a meaning to the enormous human endeavor committed to Algeria.

Only the underground extensions of the war remained obscure, and one of these I discovered, as it happened, that very day.

2/   My appointment was with the village barber.

Espanieul, unable to attend an urgent meeting organized by an Algiers industrialist, had asked me before he left for the east to go in his place and give him a report on it. The meeting had been set for the late afternoon, at Maison Carrée. For once I wanted to have a reasonably neat haircut.

Barber shops in small villages are favorite places for terrorist attacks, and troops are advised not to go there. When we did go to one, we stationed one of our men in front of the door. The barber, otherwise a thoroughly pleasant fellow, preferred not to serve army personnel.

The little shop was on a narrow and rather dark street, opposite an Arab café.

I had been there about a quarter of an hour when suddenly the curtain of big wooden beads threaded on hanging strings which served as a door was violently brushed aside and a man burst headlong into the room.

It developed that he was not a terrorist but a soldier. I shall not forget his appearance for a long time. He was tall and broad and strikingly handsome, and he looked even bigger because of his multicolored parachutist's uniform, which obviously had seen years of service. Bareheaded, with his fair hair tousled and his eyes glittering, he charged forward with his shoulders down and a bottle of beer in his hand.

At first the barber was reassured by the sight of the uniform, but he was wrong.

The man stared at me for several seconds.

"They've just told me you're J.J.S.S."

He put the bottle down on the washstand, bent forward even farther, and added, flinging the words at me with a swagger:

"I'm the one who's come to kill you." He continued to stare at me, as if electrified by the encounter.

I looked at him more attentively. I had never seen that face among our men. He must be new to the regiment.

But, although I might not know his face, his presence and the confession he had just made were not much of a surprise to me.

Since the inside tip-off which had prompted Espanieul to arrange that painful interview with the leading "activists" of Sidi-Kateb, we had been trying to learn more about the network that had set itself the patriotic task of liquidating a certain number of people, including Captain Julienne (that "dangerous extremist"!) and, as it now appeared, me.

It had not been easy. Espanieul's outburst had made him a marked man, and informers did not dare talk to him. The man in Algiers who had tipped Espanieul off was under police observation, and would no longer risk a contact for fear of making himself conspicuous to the network. The best sources of all were inside the regiment: there would obviously be fairly close relations between the civilian activists of the area and the "nationalist" volunteers who are the honest agents, in the ranks of the army, of the same political outlook.

Espanieul hardly knew them. Henry, who might not approve their methods but did share their views, knew them somewhat better. It was he, therefore, who tried to get the lowdown.

His first impression was that the co-ordination was being carried out from Paris. This was confirmed by further information that we got in Algiers. There is always, between France and Algeria, a regular traffic of liaison agents who maintain contact between civilian counter-terrorist groups and cells in the army. Some letters that had gone astray were discovered by chance and, by providing a cross-check, enabled us to learn the nature of the instructions given by the organizers in Paris to their correspondents.

A few glaring examples of this "work" have made headlines in the press, but those are only the most spectacular ones. What counts more is the routine: the intimidation, threats, kidnappings, and quiet little executions that have become part of everyday life.

And the whole outfit, aimed as it is against those who in their various jobs might try to break the vicious chain of violence, is a potent factor in the Algerian situation.

Henry had another impression, too. He believed that the "bosses," having delayed too long in ordering the more ticklish jobs to be carried out in our unit (for instance, the elimination of Julienne), had stopped counting on their original correspondents. They feared, understandably, that the men's inevitable familiarity with the victims and their comradeship under fire might have made them less "reliable." We were therefore expecting to see newly appointed executioners turning up one day soon among the new recruits.

So I was not entirely surprised when confronted in the barber shop—though I was a little excited.

The young parachutist was still standing there, staring at me. His obvious drunkenness, his blundering confession, and his hypnotized staring made me realize he would be harmless for an hour or two. Moreover, he was unarmed.

It seemed unwise to let the opportunity slip. The man would pull himself together quickly, of course, and there would be no evidence against him. With a few friends covering and helping, he would have plenty of time to form a plan of action. . . . His present state of mind made him vulnerable, but how was I to take advantage of it?

I did not have to think hard to arrive at the obvious method. My driver was waiting outside in the jeep. I asked him for his tommy-gun and handed it to the parachutist, whom I then seated behind me in the jeep. I did not look around at him once on the whole drive over the mountain road to our quarters.

As we drove I thought, with perhaps a little less concern this time, of the other young "patriot" whose tommy-gun had remained stuck in my back for a long time one summer night—the Black Angel. And one or two other pictures out of these long weeks passed through my mind.

When we arrived, I looked around.

The young parachutist was doubled up in his corner, limp and disheveled. His tommy-gun had fallen useless, as though crumpled, on the floor of the jeep. I could still hear Company Sergeant-Major Gambert's savage comparison, which cut through to the root of the matter: "When a guy hasn't been able to fire, he's had it. He won't make a comeback. It's like when it happens with a woman."

We still had to make use of the happenstance that had identified for us one of the network's more unassuming executioners, by trying to find out who was behind him. I took the parachutist into Major Henry's office.

I told Henry about the scene in the barber shop, and he could see for himself the state of the young man, red-eyed and distraught, who at that moment was trying to stand at attention and identify himself.

"Corporal Joliette, sir . . ."

Henry was sitting behind his horseshoe-shaped desk. Tall, fair, and disdainful, he was wearing a battle dress with fur-lined collar, and looked even more than usual like a country squire. He shot a contemptuous look at the killer and addressed him in an icy voice.

"What are you doing in that uniform? All the men I've known who wore that outfit were soldiers. I'm not going to see you dishonor them by dressing like them. The first thing you're going to do is to take off that uniform—understand?"

Joliette turned pale. By a sort of reflex action he lowered his head and his eyes traveled over his ample trousers and his camouflaged jacket—the uniform of so many of the heroes of the battles of Indochina and now of Algeria. He gritted his teeth and stared miserably at Henry, saying not a word.

"Do you understand what I said? Yes or no?"

The man answered in a very low voice, trembling a little: "This uniform, sir—it's my own. . . ." Dank wisps of hair fell over his eyes as he lifted his head and continued: "I was at Dien-Bien-Phu."

Henry leaped to his feet. His face was so red it looked as if he had been slashed with a riding-crop. Saint-Cyr, his father the general, the history of France, the honor of the army rose in a furious revolt within him, and he cried: "You're lying!"

Then, controlling his rage, he said coldly: "You weren't at Dien-Bien-Phu!"

And now it was Joliette's turn to feel his whole body explode. He pulled himself to a rigid attention, tossed the locks of hair back from his forehead, and looked Henry straight in the eyes. His nostrils quivering, the fumes of alcohol now dissipated, he was a magnificent sight. What had once been his pride and had since been prostituted through his weak surrender to the sorry schemes of men guided by hate and self-interest—all that had constituted his courage and his dreams and that had once made a man of him—

these elements now flowed back into his being. And the drunk standing before us became a young blond god. He began to speak in a rather solemn tone.

"Throw the book at me if you like, sir, about what happened today, about me being tight and about my filthy tricks. Call me a bastard, slap any charge on me you want, but—*not that!* Don't touch that. You've no right to. Dien-Bien-Phu—I was there, all right, and nobody can rob me of that!" And in a lower voice, as if he were reciting a sacred memory: "I was a volunteer for the jump at Isabelle on the morning of the twenty-ninth."

Henry was hard hit. What he faced went far beyond the accuracy of Joliette's army record, even beyond truth in general, and it struck at the center of his life. To Henry, Saint-Cyrian through and through, the essence of a man, his qualities and his justification for existing, was to be found in military courage. Courage was fundamental: his whole conception of the universe was based on it. This man before us, this deadbeat, could not have been one of the heroes of the siege of Dien-Bien-Phu—if he had been, what was left of the foundations of the world? Henry was fair, like Joliette, tall, like him, and almost as young, and he looked at the other man as if he were a ghost of himself, come back from the days of illusions, from a time when issues were clear and wars just.

"Listen to me. If it should happen to be true, if by some miserable chance what you say is true and you jumped with our men at Dien-Bien-Phu—*you ought to be dead.* You've no right to go on living—do you hear me?—if all you can do is dishonor yourself and foul the names of your comrades."

Joliette was breathing hard. When he spoke again, it was not as a corporal addressing his CO; he was appealing to Henry as one man to another. "D'you mean what you're saying?" he asked brokenly.

"I mean it, all right. And I've nothing else to say to you. Get out of here, and don't let me ever set eyes on you again!"

Joliette turned about and left, his shoulders hunched and his eyes on the ground, once more plunged into misery. In the office next door, which belonged to Company Sergeant-Major Peisson, he collapsed into a chair without a word.

Peisson kept the regimental records. Through the thin partition that separated him from the room where Henry had seen Joliette, he had heard everything. He had looked up the young corporal's papers, which showed that Joliette had three times been cited for bravery. There was no doubt about it: Joliette was a genuine hero.

Through Joliette and one of his friends we later learned the details Henry had preferred not to go into and the answers to the questions he had not asked. Thus we discovered the workings of the "white-hero traffic" that had been systematically organized some months ago and was rapidly expanding.

Some of the exiled leaders of various associations in Tunisia and Morocco which were out to safeguard France's position by their own methods had joined forces with their political friends in Paris and formed an action group. Between these men, determined, vengeful, and idle, and their natural allies in Algeria—in the administration, the police, the business world, and the press—a common bond of sympathy arose which soon crystallized into a decision to work together.

They decided—and this was an astute move—to recruit their strong-arm men as far as possible from soldiers with fine war records. There were many of these drifting about, men who had been thrown back into civilian life

of this note is a friend who will take you to a place where we can have a quiet chat. Please follow him."

I found these precautions strange and extremely surprising, but there was nothing I could do except follow this M. Danaud. He asked me to leave my jeep and its driver behind and accompany him on foot.

We crossed the square and followed the main street, a continuation of the Algiers road, until we came to a narrower street. The crowds were beginning to thin out, and I could see that my guide was worried by the lateness of the hour and the lack of people in the streets. When we passed one of the security patrols in parachutist uniforms who make the rounds of the thoroughfares in Maison Carrée as they do in Algiers, advancing with a characteristic shuffling step, he turned his face to the wall. I could not understand his anxiety—still less share it.

"What's all this about? Why this Cook's tour? Is Monsieur Lemarchand in some sort of trouble?"

"He'll tell you himself."

We came to a *bistro*. The menu of the fixed-price meal of the day was scrawled on the window in white and blue chalk, and three or four young people were laughing and talking around the fruit stand at the entrance. Inside, there was a crowd at the bar. The sign above the door, painted in the same kind of lettering you see at Roubaix or at Toulon, read: *Au Bouliste*. To the left of the farther window, still under the name board but a little apart, was a narrower door, which was shut. My guide rang the bell, and someone came to let us in.

We were taken into a small room opening off the back of the *bistro*—you could hear the hum of the conversations at the bar. The single window, to judge from its position, must have looked out on another street, but I could not see because its heavy curtain was drawn.

Lemarchand was there, sitting at a table, writing. He got up immediately.

I knew Pierre Lemarchand—he had come to lunch one day at the regimental mess. He was a man who made a distinct impression; although he was on the short side, his face and manner were commanding. He had amazingly vivid black eyes, and his words and his movements were as firmly under his control as the industries whose management he had taken over after his father and grandfather died.

Lemarchand is one of the Frenchmen who matter in Algeria. Independent by nature and trusting his own judgment, he never joined any of the big associations that bring pressure to bear on the Government-General, the army, and the politicians in favor of what the members believe to be the right line. Most of his colleagues belonged to such associations, but Lemarchand stood aside; others did also, but he attracted the most attention.

That was all I knew about him. Did he take any part in politics? Were there other reasons, besides his well-known love of solitude, which kept him out of the "patriotic" organizations? As I moved in a world quite different from M. Lemarchand's, I had never had occasion to consider these questions.

Danaud, Lemarchand, and I were alone in the room now. The man who had shown us in, and who appeared to be the proprietor of the *bistro*, had disappeared. Danaud remained standing, his back to the window curtain. Lemarchand offered me a chair.

"I'm sorry Espanieul wasn't able to come," he began, without any preamble, "but I'm counting on you to pass on to him what I'm going to tell you, and maybe to ask for his help. My sister was arrested at the beginning of this week, and I've had no news of her. I asked officially at the Minister Resident's office; they know nothing about it. I got in touch with another of my friends who's at the GG—you'll probably see him here in a few moments—but he can't do anything. At Headquarters they tell me it can't be the army and I'd better see the police. The gendarmes at the Sûreté swear up and down that it has nothing to do with any of their people and that it must be the troops. . . . It's the old, old story, and there's no way out. All I know is that three men in camouflage uniforms came and picked her up when she left her work on Monday night, and she hasn't come back since. So I'd like to ask Espanieul, as he knows personally someone in the Government, if he will intervene directly. At least I might find out where she is."

Lemarchand spoke in a quiet voice, without any particular feeling, as if he were describing the most ordinary things in the world. I could not get over it.

"But—arrested? Why?"

Lemarchand stared at me. There was a trace of astonishment in his eyes, as if my question had been rather silly. But then he realized that, as I knew him so slightly and had no idea of his personal life or his political opinions, I could hardly take what he had just told me as a matter of course. He began again from the beginning.

"All my apologies. I'm probably too wrapped up in my own problems. I forgot that neither Espanieul nor you had been informed about my role here."

He paused a moment to collect his thoughts, to size up the position between us and decide just what he could and could not tell me.

"The colonel indicated that, if it became necessary, I could rely on you when he was away. So I'll give you a bit of background that'll enable you to understand things better. I'm a member of a more or less clandestine group which we call the France-Algeria Society and which consists of a number of heads of businesses in the large towns here. There's nothing revolutionary or subversive about our aim: it is simply to maintain contact with our Moslem friends—those we knew before the present emergency. That's all. It's a modest aim, as you can see, but it sometimes involves us quite deeply, and it's already got some of us into 'difficulties' with the authorities.

"Naturally, I don't need to tell you that these Moslem friends aren't all on the side of 'law and order.' We don't make any distinction, though: that's the idea of our little society. If it were only a question of keeping up with the Moslems who draw their envelopes at the end of the month at the GG, you can see that it wouldn't be worth while making the effort.

"As for my sister, who goes a bit further than I do, she's an active worker for the Young Catholic Action, which Monsieur Danaud here runs. You know what the papers call 'Christian Progressives'? That's them. They've put themselves at the disposal of the priests, *curés*, and missionaries here in Algeria to help them—in whatever way they're asked to help. There again, you can see, what they're doing is very ordinary and in theory absolutely harmless. My sister didn't give me any details, but I can only imagine that this work has something to do with her arrest or her disappearance. That's about all I can tell you."

Someone knocked at the door: two light knocks close together and, after an interval, a third one. Danaud jumped, and his body remained tense. Lemarchand did not turn a hair; he twiddled his pen in his fingers for a few seconds and then said: "Come in!"

The proprietor of the *bistro* opened the door, and a rather heavy man with a gray beard came in, walking with the aid of a cane. He shook Lemarchand's hand with obvious warmth, and Lemarchand introduced him to Danaud and to me. This was Lemarchand's friend at the Government-General; his name was Vignaud, and he had belonged for many years to the industrial directorate of the GG.

"Want anything?" the *bistro*-keeper asked before he shut the door.

"No, thank you, Armand," Lemarchand said. "Just come and warn me twenty minutes before curfew. This isn't quite the time to get oneself run in."

The door closed again.

Vignaud lowered himself slowly into a chair, put his cane behind him, and placed his hands on his knees. There was a look of gentle sadness in his eyes as he addressed Lemarchand. "Well, my boy, still playing with fire?"

"Listen, old man, quite a lot of things are going to happen before it's all over—that I know. And obviously what's happening now with Françoise means a lot to me. But I'm sure of one thing. At the end of the whole story—if I'm still alive—I'm going to stay on in Algeria. Your friends aren't."

"You saw the chief the other day?" Vignaud asked.

"Yes."

"How did you find him?"

Espanieul had known that Lemarchand had been sent for by the Minister Resident the week before; he had intended to ask him about the interview, but had not seen him since.

Lemarchand shrugged his shoulders gently and played with his pen. He obviously attached no importance to the subject. "I found him the same as every other time: with his back to the wall. It's fantastic how different these men are here and in Paris. It was the same with Soustelle. In France, when they speak in the Chamber, they might be living incarnations of Algeria, the army, France's glorious past, and what have you; they're sure of themselves. But here! My friend, you can't imagine how humble they are. Your chief told me in so many words—I'm not inventing a syllable—

'I'm trapped. How can I get out?' Of course. But he won't do anything to get out; he's paralyzed now. It's too late. Anyway, I've no idea why he still wants to see me. He's always done the opposite of what I've suggested. We've nothing more to say to each other."

"I was surprised at his seeing you. Every time someone mentions your name in front of him, he says: 'Don't bother me with that Lemarchand—he's an FLN agent.'"

"Of course: I meet Arabs. If *he* had met a few more, perhaps he wouldn't be where he is. But that's all history. Now it's quite another question: they're on the way to sabotaging everything, I'm sure you must realize that. A month or two ago there were still a few Moslem leaders you could get to talk; that's all finished. There's nobody left. What with snubbing them, arresting them, interning them, and occasionally knocking them off, you've had your way. Everyone who represents anything in this country has gone over to the FLN. There are no more go-betweens left. Nice work . . .

"D'you know what's happening now? Men like me, who have every intention of dying in Algeria and nowhere else— if we want to maintain contact with Algerians, we've got to see the FLN. It won't be very long before your friends will have to arrest me. Last year it was the *fellagha,* then it became any Arab with a head on his shoulders, today it's Françoise and the 'progressives.' I warn you, tomorrow it'll be me—and one or two others whose names will shock you, let me tell you.

"We haven't any refugee apartments set up in the west end of Paris, like the gentlemen of the *Echo d'Alger.* Our country is here. So we have no choice. You know as well as I do that our future lies with the Algerian leaders, not with the lieutenant of parachutists who's patrolling the next street."

His eyes wandered over to me and scanned my uni-form. "I'm sorry. I've got nothing against officers per se—you know what I mean."

All this time young Danaud had not stirred from his posi-tion at the window; every now and then he had pulled back the curtain to see what was happening in the street. Now he sat down opposite Vignaud, the high official whom the cir-cumstances of this unexpected little meeting had put in the position—probably as much to his surprise as to mine—of representing law and order. The young man's limpid eyes were remarkably bright, as if the course of the conversation had provoked some irrepressible reaction within him and he had to say what he thought.

"Look here, sir," he said in a rather deep voice, "three of my friends have been arrested already. Françoise makes the fourth. None of them hesitated for a moment between the risks they took and the intolerable idea that the whole of our counry might be on the side of repression—"

"A new set of martyrs!" interrupted Vignaud with a fa-therly skepticism.

The young Catholic, astonished, looked daggers at him.

"Mind you, I respect their feelings," Vignaud went on. "And you know I don't approve of all the present methods. But allow me to tell you that what your friends are doing isn't serving the interests of the country much better. Help-ing the FLN, whatever your intentions and whatever your methods, in the final analysis is the same as fighting against France. It is! I know everything you're going to say about the 'real' France that isn't committed to repression and all that. You won't change the facts: everything that contrib-utes to strengthening the rebels contributes, in the last re-sort, to driving us out of this country as a part of France, even if some individual Frenchmen manage to stay on and make careers here.

"I repeat: I respect your friends. And when I talk of 'new martyrs,' I do not use the term in irony. I understand that a Christian who puts his faith and certain moral values above everything else—including the interests of his country—may feel obliged to take an anti-national attitude. You must see, though, that there are people who have things to do here other than just saving their souls, people who are here, for instance, to represent France and take care of her future, and they are bound to treat your friends as enemies."

The hubbub in the *bistro*, which had been a background noise in the little room when we arrived, had stopped.

Danaud passed his hand over his close-cropped black hair and raised his head resolutely as if preparing for a difficult attack. "You're an honest man," he said, "so I'll try to answer you—everything has been said on the subject already, by people long before us, at least once a generation, and it's probably useless to start all over again tonight. We'll remain enemies. But I'd like to commend to your future reflection just one real-life incident that happened last week. When the parachutist patrol came to my friend Flouret's to arrest him, they searched the flat and ran into Flouret's wife. Can you imagine what the commander of the patrol asked her? 'Are you a Catholic?' he said. And she told me she actually hesitated a second or two before replying.

"I'm not saying we're living under the Grand Inquisition yet. But I am saying that what's happening here extends far beyond Algeria; it concerns all of France. Fascism, in the beginning, is nothing but the acceptance of order through violence—plus propaganda. After that, it becomes a matter of habit. What's happening here would have been unthinkable even a year ago. And when the French people have really approved it, accepted it, and put their money on it, you're going to see in France what you see here now. It's inevitable. You can't maintain order through violence and lying on one side and continue to respect liberty on the other; the two are *incompatible*, and one is bound to get the better of the other. For me there's no doubt about that. And that's the reason I'm fighting against what you represent. It's not for love of the Arabs or a love of martyrdom; it's because the battle's on, right here and now, between the people who are ready to swallow, *for France*, something that approximates Fascism, or whatever you want to call it, versus those who are determined to fight it, whatever the cost."

"Are you prepared," Vignaud asked, "in the name of what you would prefer for France politically, to lose the French stake in Algeria?"

"It's the other way around. Only if we refuse to see France dishonored here shall we have a chance of staying on permanently."

M. Vignaud wagged his big head: he must have found the young Catholic's conclusions a little hasty. He stroked his beard slowly, thinking carefully. Then, looking at Danaud with affectionate concern, he replied: "I'm not sure, you know, that you're being honest enough with yourself when you answer me like that. It's too easy. I respect your position, but I'd like you to respect it more yourself. Granting all the unfortunate but inevitable consequences of the use of force, you know as well as I do that to give up the use of our superior force—at least for putting down the armed rebellion—would mean giving up French sovereignty here. There's no precedent to prove the contrary. In any case, as things are today, it's self-evident. What I'm asking you is this: in order to repudiate—at any cost, as you were saying—the habit of violence, are you prepared to lose Algeria?

"Because what I'm going to suggest to you is that to

lose the game here is the surest way of plunging the French people into a state of humiliation and bitterness and anger which would indeed open the door to what you call Fascism, as a refuge from the intolerable blow to national pride. . . . Look, my friend, it's your turn to listen to me now: you don't save a country, even morally, by making it lose battles. Defeat, and the consequences of defeat, can degrade a nation more disastrously than anything else."

Danaud rose, went to the little window, and pulled a corner of the curtain aside. Then he turned and pointed to the ceiling lamp.

"Turn it out," he said.

Lemarchand turned the switch, and the room was plunged into darkness. Danaud pulled the curtain halfway open.

The silvery light of the night filled the space around us, and the little square room resembled an aquarium. Bodies had become shadows and faces were unrecognizable. Nobody moved. Through the small square of window which Danaud had uncovered, we looked into another world. Silhouetted in the moonlight, five armed figures in uniform, emerging from this suburban street of Algiers as though from the mists of human history, slowly crossed the narrow field of the window.

"That's the patrol, all right," Danaud said. "We've got a quarter of an hour to get away before they go past again. After that, the curfew. Let's go."

He pulled the curtain across the window and Lemarchand switched the light on again. Vignaud had risen, too. I was the only one still seated, fascinated by what we had seen through the window, lost in a host of memories.

Lemarchand looked at me. "You are reminded of something, aren't you?"

I nodded. My mind was more absorbed by the echo

from the past and the transient emotion it had aroused than by the precise significance of his question.

Without waiting, he answered himself. "Well, you're wrong! This is something quite different. For the Arabs, perhaps it's the same. Maybe they feel as if they're under an 'occupation.' But us? No. Where we're concerned, we're between Frenchmen. It's quite another kettle of fish."

Gathering up his papers, Lemarchand added in a lower voice: "By bungling pacification, they're paving the way to civil war."

Chapter Two

1/ The war continued its monotonous course. Operations and encirclements succeeded night patrols; outrages and destructions followed their usual cycle. Some of our comrades were being relieved by younger conscripts.

Only rarely now were we able to go out on nomadization with our little commando squads. Our men were usually needed for the big-scale offensives that the staffs put on, with squadrons of tanks, a flight of helicopters, several batteries of artillery, and fighter cover. Such tactics were still the exception when we arrived, but they had become a habit of the war now. It was all in the cards. . . .

After returning from one of these days that were compounded of commotion, of the noises of machines, of footslogging, of the droning of airplanes and the equally monotonous certainty that nothing would come of it all, I was alone in my room for a few minutes. Or almost alone: through the thin wooden partition I could hear a heated discussion between Julienne and Henry.

Despite the daily wear and tear, I was more or less conscious of the way our feelings were becoming blunted, and I tried to use this short interval to put down in my notebook a few impressions, particularly the easily forgotten details, of a commonplace but revealing incident that concerned me personally.

The previous week I had gone to Algiers with one or two other officers to see a detachment of demobilized reservists aboard the boat back to France. On the quay I was accosted by a friend who was working in the Government-General, and he told me a story so peculiar that I thought at first he was pulling my leg. He had heard from an excellent source that I was going to be quietly "contacted" by mem-

bers of the Minister Resident's military secretariat and sub-
jected to a bit of blackmail in anticipation of my return to
France: either I would keep quiet after I was demobilized or
they would produce a scandalous dossier on me.

I was skeptical, even though he swore the story was
true. I knew, of course, that Headquarters and the Government-General kept a sharp eye on the lists of men due for
repatriation to France in order to make certain of their feelings about pacification before letting go of them, and, if
necessary, to work on their opinions. But these are things
that you only hear talked about; they couldn't happen to you.
To find yourself actually face to face with a flesh-and-blood
man who knows what he is talking about and speaks your
own language, and to hear him tell you, just as they
would in the underworld or in the movies: "If you don't
keep your mouth shut, you'll never know what hit you; we've
got the goods on you"—this just doesn't happen in real life.

And, anyway, what did they have on me?

My "treason" in the clandestine *mechtas* of the FLN,
described with such picturesque detail in Franchi's "report"?
Espanieul had already taken care of that bit of goods with
the Minister. What else was there that, even in the mind of
an official geared to the new regime in Algeria, would be
damaging enough to keep me from talking?

Still incredulous, but curious, I waited to be contacted.

A few days later I was. I was asked to call a certain man,
who, I discovered, had an extremely pleasant telephone
manner. Couldn't we have lunch together, just the two of us,
outside duty hours? he asked. I insisted that the meeting must
take place in his office, and he reluctantly agreed. Room No.
X at the Government-General: I was to ask for Major B., of
the Minister Resident's military secretariat.

Three men were in the office into which I was shown.
Major B. wore civilian clothes. There was a second major,

also of the military secretariat, in uniform, and a third man, younger than the others, from the press service.

Major B. offered me a chair, and, while the others buried their noses in the papers on their desks and apparently busied themselves with things other than our conversation, he talked to me good-humoredly. Wearing a sport jacket and puffing quietly at his pipe, he seemed quite at ease.

"Listen, my friend," he said, pointedly not addressing me as an officer as I was soon to become a civilian again, "I feel rather ashamed of bringing you to this office because what I really wanted was to have a man-to-man chat with you—one that has nothing to do with the service. I might even say that what I'm going to talk to you about has very little to do with me. However, I've got a lot of admiration for you and the work you've done here, particularly with Colonel Galland, who's a friend of mine from way back, so I wanted to put you on your guard. . . . Oh, there's nothing serious about it—in fact, I feel that in some ways this little business is rather to your credit. But you know how it is: you're going to go back to public life, and when it comes to controversies and political campaigns, something that seems natural here might do you a lot of harm with public opinion and among your readers."

The thing was taking shape. As the "friendly" phrases succeeded one another, drawing closer to the object of the interview, I thought back over those months of war. I was trying to guess just what point—naturally, there would be many to choose from—the specialists would utilize to tack what the police jargon of Algiers calls "a report to my behind." We were getting close now. . . .

"Well, here we are: that brothel you organized at Sidi Kateb—one of my colleagues in Military Security was interested in it, and at the request of the Ministry of National

Defense he prepared a report. You see what I mean: it's not very pleasant. . . . Mind you, as to the brothel itself, you can be sure I'm much too old a soldier to see any harm in that. It's not only natural, it's provided for by the regulations for troops on field service."

With an air of subtle irony, he went on: "I'd even say that it fits in with pacification! After all, if there were more brothels, there'd be fewer rapes, eh? Still, people aren't likely to see things in that light. They'll say that you used your time in uniform to go in for the white-slave trade and that you haven't wasted your time here in view of the commission you drew from this racket."

I looked at the man opposite me in fascination.

Of course there was a BMC (a Field Service Brothel, which is indeed provided for in regulations) in our area, and I knew that, as usual, the military units which gave it a permit levied a tax on it, as stipulated by regulations; the proceeds were handed over for army welfare. The idea that I should be accused of having personally taken over this respectable trade in order to add to my lieutenant's pay had never occurred to me. Why not? It was as handy as anything else.

However, for me the principal interest in the little scene did not lie in the report that Military Security was preparing—though it must have made good reading. I was concerned with the way in which a man, and a French officer at that, could suggest over a table a connection between what he had just said and my silence after I got back to France.

He ended his monologue with an air of complete detachment. "There you are. I just wanted to tip you off. I repeat, it doesn't shock me. But I can imagine it might be very awkward for you if in a few months' time they were to spring that on you without warning. I wanted to tell you about it. That's all."

That was all?

He took a tobacco pouch out of his pocket and began quietly filling his pipe as I got up to leave.

Then the other major, the one in uniform, took the latest number of the *Express* out of his drawer and broke in. "Just a moment, if you'll allow me. I'd like to take advantage of the fact that you're here to have a frank chat with you. I don't know what my fellow officer B. has been talking to you about"—of course he had heard every word—"but what I want to say is in a strictly private capacity. You see"—he showed me the markings and annotations on his copy of the *Express*—"I read your paper regularly. I don't always share its opinions, but it interests me. So what I wanted to ask you . . . Let's forget our respective positions, and don't worry about my job or the fact that you're in this building—this is simply between you and me, one man to another. What I'd like to know is: what are you thinking of writing about pacification when you get back?"

So there it was. The act had been as gross as a caricature: the honeyed tone, the little bit of staging, the role of the first man (who, in his turn, had buried his nose in his files to show he was not interested in the second part of the scenario)—and the whole scene taking place less than fifty yards from the Minister Resident's office!

At that moment I was more conscious than I had ever been before of what can happen to human nature in a war like this. How could men in responsible positions sink to the degree of vileness required to act this little scene with such apparent confidence that it would effect the desired intimidation? And the stupidity of such a game, the danger that it would backfire on them—how could they have missed seeing that?

If they had become blind, it was *by dint of despising people.* In theory, of course, they despised only the Arab.

But the Arab, however much of a gook he may be, is still a man—an unalterable fact. And what you think of the gook, in the final analysis, affects the way you look at the world. You start by kicking an animal that looks like a man but is really of another species, and, unconscious of the transition, you end up by treating a French officer as if he were a Place Pigalle pimp and asking people at the point of a tommy-gun whether they are Catholic. The truth is that contempt for human beings cannot be rationed or controlled—because eventually it corrupts.

I made notes on this very ordinary incident that night— some of my comrades had far more hair-raising experiences of the same kind—just because it *was* ordinary. To me it seemed to signify all that we had encountered here—more so, perhaps, than the absurdity of the military operations or even the existence of certain methods of interrogation.

It made me realize how, without any Franco-style land- ing from overseas or any spectacular *coup d'état*, a subtle, progressive poisoning of the Frenchman's way of thinking could lead from the degradation of this war to the degrada- tion of France itself.

All this time I could hear Captain Julienne's penetrat- ing voice through the wall of my room, and his tone in- dicated that his discussion with Henry had taken an angry turn.

Both of them were good men, but they hated each oth- er's guts. Henry resented the destructiveness of Julienne's mind; everything that Julienne said chipped away at the foundations of the soldier's world, and Henry could not stand it. Julienne did not understand that sincerity could be relative—that it could exist within a system of values which he considered was based on a lie. The result was that, simply reacting to each other's stubbornness, they often bristled. That particular day the argument was about Jouve, and Julienne had exploded.

"If you don't relieve him of his command at once, I'll insist on a transfer myself! It's not only that he's disgracing himself—I couldn't care less about that, and anyway he's been doing it so long—but he's dragging all of us down with him. I didn't come here to play ball with murderers and looters!"

"All right, then get the hell out of here! I'm fed up with your fits of conscience. Why don't you stay at home? We've no room here for people who want to play politics in the army."

Henry often confused morals with politics—and maybe he was right, for that matter.

"If you don't like the work," Henry went on, "go cleanse your conscience wherever you can. As for the rest of us, we're staying on here because someone's got to stay on. If I had to relieve all the officers and NCO's who trouble Monsieur Julienne's sensibilities, there wouldn't be any regiment left. They're all very nice, your stories. But an army in the field isn't a Sunday-school class; it wasn't I who said that, it was Lyautey. And if you think I'm disgracing myself too, well, go and tell the general. Go and tell it in Paris, go ahead and do your stool-pigeon job and get the hell out of here!"

Did they still get a kick out of these everlasting arguments? Henry and Julienne, like so many others, were at each other's throats at least three times a week. The fight always simmered down eventually—it had to. Nobody plays stool pigeon, nobody gets the hell out, everyone goes on working. And nobody is very happy.

"What more do you want?" Henry went on. "I've had

two sergeants court-martialed this week. Doesn't that satisfy you?"

It was true that Henry was doing what he could. I could not understand why Julienne kept nagging him. What did he hope to accomplish? He knew that when you punish a sergeant or a captain or have men court-martialed, you may kid yourself into thinking you've done something, but it is sheer hypocrisy. You expose men to a system that can automatically drive them into criminal behavior, and then you haul them in for that kind of behavior. Should you punish them? Of course, in theory. And then what? Inevitably, other men will react just the same way, and feelings of injustice and intolerable bitterness will continue to grow.

Julienne was aware of this. He was resurrecting a lame argument against Henry because he was furious about Jouve, or, possibly, just to pass the time. He was so well aware of it that he had secretly told me an idea I have not forgotten.

"I've discovered something," he said to me one day. "I've been reading the *Letters from Stalingrad* and, at the same time, watching what's going on with some of our men. I've discovered not only that there were Germans who weren't Hitlerites, but that there are Frenchmen who are. . . . That throws quite a lot of thinking out of gear, doesn't it?"

It does indeed. There is no one who is naturally evil, *naturally* vulgar, cruel, or prejudiced. There are situations which inflame the beast in man and there are others which nourish his soul. People who make it their business to run the lives of their fellow citizens are responsible for the situations they create. To condemn the victims of these situations as though the victims were responsible is merely to add cowardice to incompetence.

Communist propaganda has compared some of the behavior of the French army in Algeria to that of the SS in Hitler's army. That is wildly untrue. What is true is this: when you have seen in Algeria how easily men can become helpless playthings of the set-up into which they are thrown, you don't feel you have the right to condemn the men of the *Wehrmacht* any more. Individual behavior can be called reprehensible only when the behavior occurs within a collective undertaking that is not itself blameworthy.

It was Galland, as usual, with his insistence on knowing just where he stood, who one day went straight to the sensitive point. And what he discovered is of extreme importance.

He had received a general directive from the Command on the technique recommended for fighting terrorism and acts of sabotage. The implication of the limits to which the French commanders were authorized to go was so unmistakable that he found himself asking whether this did not mean we had already reached the final stage: the stage where blunders have not only become the rule, but the *official* rule.

The thing had to be settled one way or the other. So Galland sent the Commander-in-Chief's directive back accompanied by a peremptory request—on which he staked all his authority and his job—that a paragraph should be added making it clear that "*the methods regularly employed by totalitarian countries to obtain information and immediate results should be categorically rejected and unequivocally condemned.*"

Galland was summoned before the highest authorities in Algeria and in the army and told—with all due decorum, of course—that to take a stand such as he recommended would embarrass our local commands for no good reason, would hinder their work, and would serve no object but theoretical morality. In addition, his request must inevitably

arouse legitimate suspicions about the motives that inspired
it.

My room had become almost silent again. The movements of transport outside the building had slacked off. Our
men were resting up after two long days of operations and
marching. Henry and Julienne were talking more quietly;
the two of them must have discovered all over again, as
they always did, the futility of dogmatizing on the executive
level and the necessity for compromise in the area of day-to-
day decisions.

Outside, night was falling on our mountain and on the
Algerian plain—a night like so many others that had yet to
fall on this war that France is waging on herself.

I tried to make use of this unaccustomed spell of lei-
sure to assemble and analyze the reasons for the conviction
all of us felt that we were immersed in the heart of a tragedy
in which the whole future of the country was at stake. We
all accepted this feeling as perfectly reasonable—but why?

Even with men of the caliber of Galland and Espanieul there are in army life certain fields of discussion which,
by a sort of tacit consent, are not touched upon. Often we
all came close to the essence of the problem, as Julienne had
done that evening at Ouled Smar, but we were careful to
stop just short: at the heart of the matter there is a political
question.

Or, to be more accurate, there is the political expression
of the human dilemma.

The ineffectiveness of the military methods employed,
which were setting the people against France instead of isolating the rebellion, was quite clear. The moral corruption
engendered by a war turned rotten which threatened to in-

fect France itself was clear enough, too. But that was not the whole story.

If what was happening in Algeria was really going to affect the future of France, as was evident, then beyond the armed struggle with the Arabs and the behavior of some of the authorities there must exist a fundamental clash over the structure of collective life—that is to say, a political clash.

As I lived with the Algerian war and thought about it, I began to see more clearly that the end of America's four-year Civil War had settled something which went far beyond the fate of the slaves. The victory of the North had opened the way to a form of democracy for which a victory of the South would have substituted, and for a very long time, a different form of society. That war had in fact been a struggle between the democratic potential of the government and the most powerful of feudal privileges.

The most powerful feudal privilege, the one which supports the biggest and the strongest interests, which can recruit the best-armed defense groups, and which arouses the deepest feelings, is based on an enslaved race. The day that privilege is called in question, whatever the pretext, the conflict that arises is a life-and-death struggle. It will inevitably sweep in all the other conflicts after it, for the ranks will be swelled on one side by the profiteers from every kind of privilege, with their hangers-on and their heated passions, and on the other by every element which, for good or bad, fundamental or inconsequential reasons, recognizes an interest in the enemy's destruction.

Soon the very nature of power, the political content of the State, is at stake. As the immense front of the privileged, with their allies, their servants, and their dupes, solidifies in and through the struggle, as it mobilizes all the violent emotions and develops a network of interdependent interests, the State, on pain of abdication, must rely on the people and draw strength from them, the only possible ally. This force, however, can be utilized only if it is available—that is, if it is free and organized.

Julienne, who had apparently finished his free-for-all with Henry, burst into my room and stretched himself out on my cot. Clad in undershirt and trousers, and obviously tired, he seemed, half seriously and half in jest, prepared to launch into a discussion of the "big problems."

I told him what I had been thinking: how what had happened politically in the American people's struggle among themselves on the pretext of the Negro question, ending in the overthrow of the feudalists, seemed the sort of thing that might mark the destiny of France, in another form, through the violent developments of the Algerian tragedy.

Julienne took from my bedside a bottle of lotion which I had got from Paris (and which described itself, not without some justification, as "the last word for the feet") and began to revive his poor soles, worn out by hours of marching. Rubbing one's feet was a good way of thinking when we were off duty, and Julienne continued to rub as he started talking.

"I quite agree. But what does that mean when you get down to brass tacks? That you won't get what we might call a 'non-fascist' solution of the business here except through a sort of upside-down February 6, with the State telling the feudalists where to get off instead of kowtowing to them. It's not as easy as all that, my friend. The conspiracy you want to smash is not made up of only a few big settlers, one or two newspaper proprietors, and their policemen; that's just a prettified view of affairs. No, what you're up against is everything with direct or indirect interest in exploiting the Algerian people—and that takes in a good deal of territory, not just in Algeria, but in France, too. Look at all the people who are tied up by economic, social, or moral solidarity to the 'patriots' of Algeria, plus—and here's the key to it—all those whose position in society would be jeopardized if the State really went through with the challenge to your 'Southerners.' Anyone can see that at the end of such a struggle, the big upheaval would be in France far more than in Algeria. I agree, the real question rests on the nature of the regime. But"—Julienne gestured to emphasize his point—"do you believe in the regime?"

It was a question without an answer, a question that only despair could ask. How could you not believe in it? How could you abandon the hope that before the final act in this African imbroglio, in which the fate of France was at stake, new forces would materialize which would plunge into the political battle over Algeria, shatter the war conspiracy, and, of necessity, transform the country's institutions to pave the way to a free future? And yet . . .

"Because," Julienne went on, "I'm going to tell you what, unfortunately, is a lot more likely to happen. Your 'Southerners' rule the roost, in Algiers and in Paris. That's the first point. And they're not going to quit. This policy in France, and this war, can only result in defeats. What you think is that there'll be a blow-up in France one fine day and that public opinion will be aroused to the point of forcing a showdown here. That's logical. A revolution like that would be logic itself. Unfortunately, we're not even free to make our own revolutions now. What'll happen will be quite different. Pretty soon the Powers who rule our little world will impose a settlement of this whole business which will stop the war, prevent any rough stuff—and, of course, turn us out of here. In a friendly way. And the day you see a settlement of that kind, Algeria will have ceased to be Worry Number One for Frenchmen—except that the 'Southerners' will have proved that they were the real powers *in*

France. The fate of Algeria will be a whim of the future. And France's future will be settled for years to come—just as the future of Spain was once upon a time."

Perhaps what Julienne believed was reasonable. Horribly reasonable. But the future had not been written yet, and France was not yet dead.

2/ The war went on. . . .

Helicopters are beautiful and formidable machines. They deposit you at dawn in the middle of a faraway *jebel.* Then you have a whole day's marching to get back, while they are off picking up other men for another scuffle—and evacuating the wounded.

Since operations were calling for more men than before, we often found ourselves, toward the end of my time in Algeria, joining other units in neighboring sectors.

That particular day we were in the eastern sector, too far from our quarters for us to be able to get back by nightfall. So we spent the night at the HQ of Colonel Piau, who was commanding the sector. Fortunately, we had brought bivouac tents. It had been a tiring day, uneventful and tiring. I had been with Henry, who was responsible for part of the disposition of troops. He had already completed his tour of duty, and had applied for repatriation to France: this war wasn't for him. But his application had been refused: there just weren't enough officers, and he was forced to stay on.

At the beginning of the afternoon, at siesta time—which had become the favorite hour for surprise attacks—we had flushed out a group of rebels who had taken refuge in a *mechta.* At the end of the skirmish, one of our men, whose best friend had just been killed, had vented his misery and anger on the still-breathing body of a *fellagha* on the verge of death: he had torn the two little red woolen rank-badges off the rebel's uniform, which was just like ours, and spat in his face. Two of his comrades had been so shocked that they reported it to Henry. Punctilious as always, Henry assembled the men of the depleted detachment, personally put the rebel lieutenant's stripes back on his shoulders, and ordered joint military honors for the two corpses, the Frenchman's and the Moslem's.

As usual, the march home was an endless footslog and a rest for the mind. With us were a few old acquaintances and many new faces, for the new draft had brought us young trainees along with a few officers and NCO's as our reservists took their leave.

When we arrived at the HQ of the regiment of dragoons where we were to spend the night, all of us had an irresistible desire to fling ourselves down on the ground and sleep. But Henry and the officers received a command invitation from Colonel Piau to stop in at the hut he used as an office.

Entering this wooden-walled structure after eight hours in the field, we felt we were arriving at a glittering reception. There were women. For once there were women. Women in colorful clothes, women's shoulders, women's voices . . . Colonel Piau was very dignified, very much the head of the household, and in complete command. Our Espanieul was there too, although he almost never, these days, felt like exploding into his wild laugh that suggested a jungle beast, frustrated as he was in his hopes for heroic action. He had taken hard his discovery that the people in the saddle were the contemptuous, well-organized forces against which, one June day in 1940, he had launched an uncalculating battle —a battle from which he and a few others had thought they had come out the victors. In a corner of the room, a glass in his hand, Espanieul was flirting in a distant, listless way with one of the young women, as if he were acting merely out of habit or politeness.

By and large, though, the little gathering was a pleasant one. The arrival of visitors from France never left us indifferent. Whoever they might be—journalists, deputies, officials, family connections—and whatever they looked like, their presence brought to everyone a sense of things far away and friendly, mirroring a certain affection. This time the newcomers were theater people.

Our host called for silence, raised his glass, and began to speak emphatically—he must have liked speaking.

"Gentlemen . . . We're almost all of us here now—I don't imagine Captain Julienne and his detachment will be long in getting back—so I propose, in your behalf and in that of our men, to thank the X—— *pastis* company, who are so kindly touring Algeria to bring a little entertainment to our troops. They're doing a great job, and we're all very grateful to them. . . . And now I should like to add that, when our guests of tonight return home, we hope they will act as our ambassadors to our fellow countrymen. We hope they'll tell them at home what's going on here, about the work that's being done by France and by the French army in this magnificent country, and that they will tell them particularly that we shall never agree to a surrender—that we're carrying our colors high and that we're showing the world that Algeria is France. . . . Gentlemen, our guests!"

The manager of the company, a Marseillais with a friendly accent, looked like the singer Tino Rossi with a bit less hair. Impressed by the level to which Colonel Piau had raised the little gathering, he contented himself with stumbling through a few pleasant words of thanks, raising his glass of *apéritif*. Then everyone went to the supper table for a quick cold meal before the music-hall show that was to be given in the movie theater of the neighboring village.

Piau was a colonel of the classic style, the most common type—no nonsense and the honor of the army, everything's going splendidly. And Espanieul, whom I watched with pitying eyes, made a visible effort at the beginning of the meal to contain himself. But he ended by exploding.

"I hope you'll excuse me, sir," he began in a cold voice, "but I don't see why the presence of visitors from France should oblige us to talk nonsense. On the contrary, if they can do us a service when they get back, they'd do better to tell the truth: that the fine gentlemen who are running us, whether they wear star-spangled uniforms or morning coats, don't understand a thing and are leading us straight to disaster. That our troops are doing their job the best they can, but that what they're being asked to do is stupid and degrading. And that if things don't change, the army will end up by revolting, too. As you know, that has started already. Let them say all this when they get back to Marseilles, and it may do us some good."

After a few seconds of surprise, Piau retorted in the manner we knew as well as we knew Espanieul's arguments.

So while the *pastis* comedians listened not very attentively—they were more interested in discovering whether vehicles would be available to take them back to Algiers that night or whether they would have to sleep here—the usual argument of every soldiers' mess in Algeria developed once more, with a good deal of sincere emotion voiced on either side. Espanieul wanted to revolutionize the army's methods; Piau replied that the army was beyond reproach, that the only danger lay in the timidities and hesitations of France. Espanieul thundered that the so-called "pacification" had become a joke played on the French people, that the army was disgracing itself by supporting lies. Piau, sounding like the official communiqués, countered that everything would have been settled long ago if we hadn't been betrayed by foreign powers and newspaper campaigns. The tone of the discussion mounted to a violent pitch, but there was no real hatred, for the two men were obscurely aware of the one thing which bound them more than their differences separated them: the feeling of their impotence.

After dinner we were taken down to the theater in the village square, where a big crowd had gathered. It was apparent that among all the units taking part in the series of operations in the sector, few men had found difficulty in overcoming their tiredness when they had an opportunity, which did not occur often, to enjoy an evening's entertainment. Groups of them were still crowding into the packed hall. Everyone was doing his level best to make himself small, to occupy only half a chair, in order to make room for his buddy.

In a hushed silence the impresario of the company read his little introductory speech, which paid equal tribute to the gallant soldiers who formed the audience and the great Marseilles manufacturer who was taking care of their morale. What he said did not matter. The fact that he was on a stage and that he was talking was all that was asked of him. The crowd loved it. There was endless applause when he stopped.

The show began. It was what you would have expected. The singers, the magicians, the comedians, the impersonators, the acrobats with whom we had had dinner appeared one after another and did their numbers. The acts were announced by a lady in a white ballet skirt, and her every appearance was hailed with a roar of applause.

During a short intermission I strolled in the village square with a woman social worker billeted at Colonel Piau's HQ. I was curious to hear about her difficult job—and also to hear the forgotten sound of a woman's voice in the night air.

She knew our young soldiers from an angle quite different from mine, for they talked to her more freely. And as she told me of their confessions, anxieties, stories of troubles that had to be forgotten, she, who a moment ago had seemed a plain and mundane figure, now seemed to epitomize all the graciousness of being a woman.

The intermission ended, but we continued our stroll in the now empty square. At intervals a patrol would pass by, and when it had gone, the evening was like an evening in peacetime. From time to time the laughter or the applause in the theater would reach us as a wave of muffled noise—as in the main street of a sub-prefecture in the south of France. On the heights, there were a few wreaths of mist and the peacefulness of the night. The dimensions of the war, which had seemed to us illimitable all the months we had been closeted here, shrank to their truer, relative size beside the daily problems—as concrete as they are serious—of man's estate.

What this girl was describing was the reality even more deeply felt. The monotony of letters, the misery of loneliness, the void in so many heads and so many hearts, the requests for money made with such an insistent gentleness that it is heart-rending not to know which way to turn to find it, the friends at home who have forgotten your existence and those here who take you for a creature you don't recognize, the diarrhea, the longing to be in a hospital, the difficulty of living, and the simplicity of the tragedies—all the inhuman jungle, inevitable and accepted, that lies behind the façade of a society that calls itself organized.

From one ridge to another, the light signals were answering each other. Were they ours or the enemy's? Our encirclements and their ambushes were being planned for tomorrow, just as the dead of today, our own and theirs, were lying side by side.

When we returned to the theater at the social worker's suggestion, I had still not seen Julienne. By the diffused light coming from the stage, I tried to identify his big gray head among the packed rows of people, but I could not find him.

I was looking too near at hand. There, close to the stage and facing the audience through the darkness, I recognized Julienne's big silhouette, his arms folded on his chest, his head resting, as if it were a little heavy, against a wall.

We went and joined him.

"What are you doing there?"

Julienne had become taciturn in the last few weeks and often seemed not to hear what you said to him. There was an interval now before he answered me. Motioning gently with his chin and his eyes at all those faces, those uniforms, those young men packed one against another as they concentrated on the show, he said at last:

"I'm looking at them."

The man on the stage was giving an imitation of Maurice Chevalier, and the crowd, wild with delight, let out a roar of laughter which echoed from the wooden walls. All those faces we were watching reflected the almost forgotten experience of being happy. There they were, Mauré, Bunny, Gambert, Bodard, Canu, the Black Angel, a world away from the difficulties of their service and the anxieties of their lives. And there were the new arrivals, too, younger men who had yet to discover here, with humility, the serfdom of their country and the beast within each of them. In the endless laughter that shook them and set the air around us aquiver, we found once more a joy in life and a passionate need to hope. The freshness of these young people, coaxed from them by their pleasure, was pouring out into the hall. Drawn from the very depths of them, from beneath the daily impotence and the daily fears, the sound of youth seemed to cut across the scorn of the organized world, projecting into the future an appeal, stronger than slavery, more profound than agony, more lasting than war—an entreaty for another fate, for a future that embraces freedom.

"Sure," said Julienne slowly, addressing no one, "maybe the gooks aren't men; but then all of us are gooks. . . ."

Letters from Algerian Army Comrades

My Algerian army comrades have written to me after reading this story. Their letters, whether they express approval or criticism, are reproduced here.

Letters from men who are not in a position to express themselves in public are signed with the names of the characters with whom these men have identified themselves.

I thank them for their testimony. Their letters show, without exception, that beyond the differences of opinions and of temperaments there remains the reality of the facts—the things we endured and witnessed together.

J.J.S.S.

LETTER FROM COLONEL "GALLAND"

My dear Servan-Schreiber,

I had lost the habit of the gray, uneventful days which I've found again back in Brittany.

I can't get out of my mind the pictures of Bou Zegra, of the Mitidja, and of the roadstead at Algiers under a blazing sun, and when I reread your story I wanted also to savor once more the bitter taste of our talks about the chances of a future for France in Algeria, Espanieul's impassioned outbursts, and Julienne's down-to-earth realism. . . .

It's all absolutely true. I'd believed, as Marcus did, that the army's paramount job was to gain the confidence of the people, free them from terror, and help them to overcome their wretchedness and passivity. It was with genuine excitement that I watched, despite the appalling official indifference and inertia, the progressive organization of the team of civilians, regular officers, and young reserve officers who had made up their minds, in spite of everything, to increase the number of contacts and to set up and protect construction jobs, medical posts, and schools. Your nomad commandos, reinforcing as they did the activities in the *douars* of the all too few SAS, were perhaps going to help our men discover themselves, and to restore to the whole system the meaning of its mission and a new dynamism and enthusiasm.

The very first thing we had to do was to hold out at any cost against the slow degradation of truth which Marcus denounced.

We also had to have the courage to take a few more risks, if you like, but at the same time to refuse to treat all Moslems as suspects from the word go; to marshal all our faith and all our energy to smash the monstrous mechanism of a subversive war whose absurd fate you describe so well and which still tends to identify the Arab people as a whole with the rebels.

Marcus may have thought that it was too late, that any hope of pacification was perhaps too late, and that all we could do was to save ourselves from our own debasement.

I can't believe that. To do so would be to despair of ourselves; to give up, after formulating a liberal policy, because we hadn't the energy to make it work; to run the risk of yielding, through weakness, to the temptation to use shameful methods, and to the vain hope of a solution by mere brute force.

Even today, without denying the spiritual values of Islam, is it not by means of a France restored to herself again that the Moslems could find the best solution to their agonizing problems and take their place in a modern, rapidly changing world?

This is their big test, but it's ours even more.

Is there no more in France that breed of men with inflexible moral standards and unflinching character who could renovate the outdated institutions of the country and of the army and restore to us the sense of our great national traditions? Are we yet once more going to let ourselves be driven out, powerless and disillusioned, despairing of our future?

I refuse to believe that our young people will continue to be blind to the facts. It is their fate that is at stake in Algeria and in the Sahara, and this great hope may be France's only hope of a last chance.

I leave you, my dear Servan-Schreiber, to your dangerous job of journalist. As for me, I am deriving a selfish pleasure from the few weeks of holiday I've allowed myself, but my peace of mind is troubled by this cowardly inability to grapple with the great tasks that beckon us.

COLONEL "GALLAND"
Companion of the Liberation
Legion of Honor

LETTER FROM COLONEL BARBEROT

My dear Servan-Schreiber,

You were under my command for six months in Algeria, and I can therefore hardly leave unanswered certain criticisms which, through you, touch directly on me.

Such criticisms as may be aroused by your position as a journalist and a politician are no concern of mine, and it is not my intention to answer them.

I can only say here what I said officially in the various reports on you which I was asked for by the Minister of National Defense and the Secretary of State for the Armed Forces (Army).

"When M. Servan-Schreiber reported to 531 half-brigade in July, I told him once and for all, in the presence of his battalion commander, that he would be treated as Lieutenant Servan-Schreiber as long as he behaved like any other officer, and that it was none of my business what he had been before and what he would be afterward, that being the responsibility of the Government, which had had every right to judge whether his recall to the colors was advisable. . . .

"It is none of my business, therefore, to pass judgment on him from a political point of view, but as an officer, and in that capacity I can only say that he gave me every satisfaction.

"He was looked on and treated in the half-brigade like any other lieutenant, though more was probably asked of him than of others because of his intelligence, his energy, and the obvious interest he took in his job. . . . On the other hand, I must agree that Headquarters, the Minister Resident, his personal staff, and the departments under him treated him not merely as an officer but as a journalist and a politician; the special attention they paid him was not at all that which an ordinary lieutenant would get. . . ."

I think, moreover, that the text of the mention in dispatches of which you were the subject in connection with the engagement of August 31, in particular, constitutes a sufficient answer to any criticism.

I also said in these reports to the authorities that, although in the course of your story you frequently changed details in order to make it difficult or impossible to identify specific places, circumstances, or people, that did not prevent your story from being true.

Your account is all the more valid as it does not portray incidents of an accidental character, but a day-by-day reality of which you were able to observe certain aspects and which seems to me to be the picture of the war as it appears in Algeria.

What stands out in your story and is the essential point is that the policy of pacification which was accepted by the electorate and by Parliament is not being applied in Algeria. There is no need to be an exhaustive observer, merely an impartial one, to see that the methods now being applied, on the administrative as well as on the military level, run absolutely counter to pacification.

To give voice to this essential truth, which is the very reason why General de Bollardière asked to be relieved of his command, can in no way prejudice the morale of the army. The army today is bitterly aware of a situation for which it is not responsible, but for which it fears it will one day have to shoulder the responsibility.

What does prejudice the morale of the army is the series of disasters which has dotted our history over the last seventeen years. "We shall win because we are the strongest"; "We've come to the last quarter of an hour"—these slogans do not go over with the army any more.

What may seriously prejudice the morale of the nation is to let the people believe that everything that could be tried has been tried. In the face of difficulties so apparently insoluble, the only way out would be that of surrender.

No one can deny the right of a Government in a state of war to adopt measures curtailing certain essential freedoms, including the freedom of expression, and to take the view that certain truths may be dangerous and therefore blameworthy. But these restrictions of freedom are legitimate only in so far as they serve the policy that has been decided on and approved by the electorate; otherwise, they can only be ascribed, as is the case here, to despotism.

Finally, because you were the first of the demobilized reservists to describe the reality and because General de Bollardière was the first and the only man to oppose publicly the methods that are leading to a defeat, we are now being accused of having "covered up" in our units those very brutalities and blunders against which we fought by every means we could. "The bigger the lie, the better its chances of being believed. . . ."

> ROGER BARBEROT
> *Companion of the Liberation*
> *Legion of Honor*
> *Colonel, OC 531 DBFA*
> (*demobilized*)

LETTER FROM MAJOR "HENRY"

My dear Servan-Schreiber,

I don't need to tell you that, while I feel a warm friendship for you as a soldier and admire your qualities as a man and an organizer, that does not mean I share your political views.

I won't take sides for or against the publication of your story. But I fully recognize its merits. Your descriptions are good, your analyses of characters are generally accurate, though you sometimes tend to underestimate opponents and to endow friends with too many virtues. However, this doesn't shock me, for the reverse is often done.

I belong to a race which is probably extinct nowadays, that of the out-and-out soldier whose only love is the army and whose only religion is worship of his country. Our worn-out intellectuals would probably classify me in the category of half-wits, a hangover from the time of Déroulède, but it is difficult for a man worthy of the name to change his personality to fit in with every chance encounter and attraction.

Your friend François Mauriac doesn't pass judgment on God because he reduced Sodom to ashes and has punished us all for the original sin committed by Adam. In the same way, I can't criticize my country because it is waging war in Algeria.

War is an unpleasant thing, I know better than most, for I've been at it for thirteen years, but it's sometimes necessary when it's a question of avoiding something worse.

Our average politicians, who stand for the dying-dog policy, hammer into the electors' ears ridiculous slogans such as "peace," "disarmament," etc. The pacifists are delighted and vote for them in droves, and when a catastrophe like '39–'40 comes along, nobody thinks of charging them with a share of the responsibility.

Now, these so-called colonial wars, such as Indochina yesterday and Algeria today, these wars which everyone criticizes and which the ignorant public doesn't consider as really national affairs, are in fact no more than the latest form of the struggle in which we're engaged with our present-day enemies. They're what the theorists call revolutionary wars. To try and settle this sort of war by political means is a utopian idea, since the enemy's object is not the improvement of conditions for the natives, but our complete eviction.

The solution of all these problems therefore seems to be a strong central Government, capable of according certain freedoms, though not at the price of losing everything in the name of freedom, capable also of winning the respect of people who may be different from us but who are linked to us by a common destiny. And, finally, the essential condition of success is a Government in a strong enough position to make itself respected by the foreign powers who are out for the destruction of what we have achieved, because of their own interests and political aims.

There, as I see it, is the key to the problem. As for the rest, the guilty consciences or the theoretical arguments of the heroes of your story cover only very special aspects of the question and don't offer any solutions. They make me think of a doctor with a patient who has cancer and who focuses his whole treatment on curing him of a cold in the head.

Finally, since I look upon you as a dynamic person with great qualities, I've only one regret to express, and that is that you're not on my side. The future will show, probably sooner than we think, which of the two of us was right. I'm sure we shall then admit our mistakes as good sports.

MAJOR "HENRY"
Legion of Honor

LETTER FROM CAPTAIN JULIENNE

My dear friend,

Even your enemies have done me the honor of recognizing me in that good old simpleton of a Julienne, and in one wretched anonymous letter addressed to a number of Paris papers they have accused the individual represented by Julienne of treason and embezzlement.

I don't really know how to tell you just what I feel—a truck is making an appalling racket right beside me. I'm standing up and writing on the hood of my jeep. We've been waiting in the mist since four o'clock this morning to go into action. Part of the battalion is with me. The fog is holding us up. But waiting befits a soldier. I've spent a lifetime waiting.

I like your story:

1. *Because you state with moderation facts that are absolutely correct.*

2. *Because these things had to be said.*

3. *Because I have the same ideas as you, maybe.*

Above all, because you are defending the French army and the dignity of France; because you define the real problem: the struggle against a reborn Fascism, against lies, and against the flood of eyewash we get from Algiers.

To count on violence to restore order in the end is the beginning of Fascism, sure enough.

The honor of the army doesn't enter into the business. I wonder what is eating some of our brass. Where do they get the idea that you're attacking the army?

You'll find people who think like Galland, Marcus, and Espanieul everywhere. . . .

It's not everywhere you'll find the exacting conscience of a Galland, the mastery, the intelligence of Marcus, or the strength and genius of Espanieul.

But everywhere there are big fat heads or little heads that want to save Algeria and want to keep it inside a French community—without sacrificing the honor of France.

In Algeria more than anywhere else we often have to push ahead because we must save it despite the ideas of certain Frenchmen here who are capable of losing Algeria even quicker than Russia will lose Hungary.

It was chance that brought us together: Galland, Espanieul, you, me, and Marcus. Marcus and Espanieul I'd known for fourteen years; Galland only by name. I read the *Express*. I could well have dispensed with knowing Henry. . . .[1]

I'm picking up where I left off; I was interrupted by the operation. I'm in the same place as yesterday, after spending the night in an ambush.

Today I'm sitting in the jeep. The weather's clearing up a little. The trucks and tanks are still getting on my nerves. I'm a little sleepier than yesterday. There's nearly an inch of mud and rain. And we're probably in for another week of it. But I've got a tough constitution (as you say) and a happy nature. Anyway, I believe that even men (me, in any case) who hate what's going on are living like lords in the midst of all this.

That's Geronimo, I believe, who just went by. He's always the same, heroic, childish, tough, and nice. I've got to get back on the job.

I can't seem to finish this letter. There's an infernal noise. I'm going to send you these notes just as they are. What else can I do? People are talking to me from every direction.

And if you can't make anything out of this rubbish, you can tell yourself it comes from your old friend.

CAPTAIN ''JULIENNE''
Legion of Honor

P.S. In Marcus's notes, which I've kept, there were a few lines which I'm sending on to you:

---

[1] Passages implicating third parties in what they might regard as a libelous manner have been cut out of the texts of the letters published here.

"Must we conclude that the struggle is lost and abandon ourselves to despair? Not at all . . . France's young men, drafted or recalled to the colors, are some of the best the country has ever produced. Everything can still be saved if only the army finds the strength to cure itself of its faults. But there's not much time left."

LETTER FROM LIEUTENANT ANTOINE

This letter will appear under my name if I can get the necessary permission; otherwise, would you please consider it as a bit of private correspondence?

[*The Ministry of National Defense gave its official permission to Lieutenant Antoine for the publication of this letter.*]

My dear Servan-Schreiber,

You were good enough to ask me to tell you in a letter what I thought of your story entitled *Lieutenant in Algeria.* When you did that, and it's all to your credit, you took a big risk—to begin with, because of our very different, indeed completely opposite, opinions. . . .

To go into the problem with any thoroughness would call for much more than a letter, so I will confine myself to the facts with which I am personally acquainted and content myself, for the moment, with answering the following questions:

Was the publication of your story appropriate or desirable?

Will reading it give non-expert public opinion an accurate picture of the Algerian campaign and the problem of Algeria?

I honestly believe that the answer to both questions must be: No.

As to the first, the clearest proof is the fact that certain papers, which can hardly be called nationalist, thought your articles justified their printing heavy front-page headlines: TORTURE IN ALGERIA DENOUNCED.

I have also replied No to the second question, although, generally speaking, there is no question of the authenticity of the facts you relate, whether they concern our activities or those of the outlaws. However, the way you present them, and the background you provide for them, together with the necessary changes in people, times, and places, give your testimony a certain coloring which cannot be regarded as that of the reality.

Finally, your silence on certain crucial points can only add to the present confusion in people's minds.

Among other examples, you leave the circumstances of the death of the Moslem killed by Geronimo still in doubt. In the same way, you talk of M. Maroni, the unpleasant settler, whom I remember very well. You haven't forgiven him his astonishing idea of hospitality, a completely empty room and a lavatory for four officers, when the accommodation at his disposal, his wealth, and the circumstances surely laid him under a certain obligation to be generous. Talking of that, another person I remember is M.G., who provided a wretched servant's room for Colonel Galland's quarters, but you must admit that these were two isolated cases and that they don't represent, expressed as a percentage, more than one or two per cent of the European population.

But if you think of the wonderful welcome we got from Madame C., who, like so many other people, invited soldiers to eat with her every Sunday, of MM. L——, O——, and B—— at Sidi Moussa, J—— d'H——, Th——, and D—— at Fondouk, and M. J—— at Maréchal-Foch, who went all out, with their families helping them, to try to entertain our men and give them a better Sunday dinner, you must agree that these people—whom we were defending, I grant you the point, but just as we would have defended Bretons and men of Provence—treated the army very well and very generously.

I don't know much about the story you mix Jouve up in. But I know the man, and I think you've blackened him. I'm afraid that there, too, you've let yourself be carried away by your antipathy for him.

Without belittling the force of some of the arguments put forward by the gallant Julienne, whom you portray as a regular officer, I think it ought to be made perfectly clear that Julienne is a regular officer only on the books. He was on half-pay for many years, he forgot to take part in the Indochina campaign, though it lasted a good eight years, and you must therefore allow me not to consider him as one of us, though he wears the same parachutist beret that I do.

It's too bad you didn't emphasize that, though my contacts with Ramdane did really take place, it had been laid down from the beginning that the exchange of ideas must be founded on the premise that Algeria would remain French and that the aim was to be the application of the Minister Resident's directives—directives which, it is true, in their application met with as much obstruction from the rebels as from the Frenchmen of Algeria.

The Black Commandos didn't behave as you say, and it's a shame. No reflection on the idea, which I think is a very valuable one, but the human material at your disposal stood in the way of any success. These people weren't sold on the idea; they were just following Major Henry, and if you hadn't had the backing of this regular officer, a veteran of the Far East campaign, you wouldn't have had a single volunteer. You remember what one of our men told the general who asked him why he'd wanted to serve in the commandos: "We get too browned off in the post, that's why I preferred going along."

I didn't know there were prefabricated searches in the regiment, and I never heard Colonel Espanieul refer to them, even in his off-the-record briefings; since I commanded one of the three battalions, I can be certain that never happened with me. . . .

I think you should have told your readers that, while in our conversations I might have been the champion of the use of force, I was also the only one who sent up for court-martial two men who were guilty of brutality, which shows that firmness is not opposed to good conduct.

I do genuinely feel that the confidence you enjoyed and the position you held—you were in fact Major Henry's adjutant—would have allowed you to intervene, with some chance of success, to stop certain excesses, at least on the regimental level. Without any ill-feeling, but out of simple regard for the truth, I am bound to say that the discipline and the behavior on operations of the unit to which you belonged were, to say the least of it, questionable.

Finally, notwithstanding the details which you were good enough, at my request, to embody in your story, I should like to take the opportunity I've been given to give a rapid sketch of my opinions on second lieutenants.

It is true that most of them disappointed me a lot on arrival; that was when I told you of my impressions. I passed judgment on them harshly because they were intellectually and materially dishonest. What can you say for men who draw an officer's pay from the State and then don't carry out the duties of the rank, and, moreover, put forward a dubious ideal to cover up for their lack of enthusiasm for operations?

If they had been real men, and logical, they would have

surrendered their rank-badges and the advantages that went with them, but they didn't.

Then, in time, as the difficulties of day-to-day life engendered the team spirit without which no collective body could survive, they became new men; with one or two exceptions, I felt when I sent them back to civilian life that I was saying good-by, not to subordinates, but to colleagues.

On another level, and with natural differences, what I've said is equally true of our rank-and-file reservists.

To sum up and to conclude, I would stress one fact. You maintain that acts of brutality were the result of a method of pacification, or were the method itself. I think, on the contrary, that they were only individual acts due to lack of discipline or the individual reactions, regrettable but not without some cause, of certain people particularly affected by the terrorism.

LIEUTENANT M. ANTOINE
Legion of Honor
Airborne Troops

LETTER FROM COMPANY
SERGEANT-MAJOR "PEISSON"

Dear Lieutenant,

Daddy Peisson has read your story *Lieutenant in Algeria* with a great deal of interest. The changes you have made in no way deprive the story of its vigor and don't alter the reality of the facts.

The atmosphere is there, too.

The denunciation of certain mistakes cannot be regarded as any sort of encouragement to the rebellion, and restrictions on the freedom of the press won't change anything at all.

It was the horrible atrocities of the "outlaws," which you also describe in your story, that provoked certain over-simple methods of repression: that's why it's necessary to keep a cool head and know what you're doing.

I wish the realistic and human formula of the Black Commandos could be generally adopted. Our reservists and their NCO's did finally understand it. . . .

I don't think one ought to ignore the excellent work done by the volunteer NCO's (veterans of Indochina and regulars). They adapted themselves perfectly to the very special form military action took in Algeria, and our battalion was what it was because of their technical competence and their gallantry under fire.

Our Air Force reservists adapted themselves quickly and courageously to a kind of life that was completely new to them, thanks to their willingness and also to the example of the volunteer NCO's whose recruitment, it is true, was not strictly in accordance with the traditional bureaucratic rules.

Ideological conceptions and party dogmas don't amount to much once you've faced up to this imperative task: "Algeria's got to stay French."

The real interests of the natives themselves require it, those of the Europeans of Algeria and of France and the French Union dictate it. With a National Union Government, and trusting in our magnificent army, this objective will be attained.

The memories I retain of my service with this battalion of Air Fusiliers are as dear to me as those I treasure of my years with the Free French Forces, from the Chad to the Rhine, when I had the honor of serving under the orders of General de Gaulle.

My best wishes to all my officers and to all my comrades —reservists, volunteers, and regulars alike.

> COMPANY SERGEANT-MAJOR ''PEISSON''
> *Military Medal*

LETTER FROM QUARTERMASTER-
SERGEANT GOULAY

My dear friend,

I recognize myself in Company Sergeant-Major Gambert.

In spite of some differences in views of politics as a whole, the veracity of the facts is beyond question, and you have rightly emphasized the present methods of pacification.

My daily contacts with the Moslem people of Algeria have always given me the impression that they are profoundly attached to France. The present policy offers them "rights" which they don't care a damn about, whereas sound and elementary reforms—for example, raising the standard of living, agrarian reform, and, above all, abolition of the excessive privileges of the *big* settlers—would soon restore peace and a brotherly Franco-Moslem coexistence.

I won't say any more on these subjects. You know my ideas and the method we employed with such success in the Black Commandos: exemplary severity with the criminal outlaws; restoration of confidence to the victimized people by a new definition of our relations, founded this time on fraternity and justice.

> ANDRÉ GOULAY
> *Quartermaster-Sergeant* (*Reserve*)
> *Military Medal*
> *"Volunteer of the French Union"*

LETTER FROM PRIVATE B.

Dear Lieutenant,

I am one of the people who have followed with interest and a great deal of attention the fascinating stories which bring back to life for me my six months with the colors. I recognized the people you mentioned under imaginary names: Espanieul, Julienne, Galland, Henry, Gambert—and good old Peisson, who was a real father to us.

You have had the courage to tell the public what is really happening in Algeria, and you have done it frankly, exactly as you lived it, and felt it, too. You have expressed what many reservists felt, too, believe me. I was one of them. . . .

I was with you, too, that day when the young parachutist burst into the barber shop like a bomb, and the rest of it, when you gave him my tommy-gun.

Do you remember, too, the dressing-down you gave that party of African Light Cavalry on the Sakamody road? Their machine-gun carriers were piled with sacks full of chickens, chickens they'd pinched from the *mechtas* around there. The worst of it was that that area came under a post belonging to our unit. If you remember, the commandos of this post had started an excellent job of making contact with the Moslem population, and in a few minutes the cavalry had undone all our work. We'd lost the people's confidence. And perhaps we'd made that many more rebels!

I am with you with all my heart, sir, and I am expressing the feelings of many of my reservist comrades.

P. B.

Demobilized Reservist
Your jeep-driver in Algeria

A Note on the Author

Jean-Jacques Servan-Schreiber was born in 1924.

After entering the Ecole Polytechnique in 1943, he left France at the age of 19 to join General de Gaulle's Free French Forces in Africa. He ended the war as a fighter pilot.

Going into journalism after he finished at the Polytechnique, he was first an editorial writer on foreign affairs for the Paris newspaper Le Monde. *Then in 1953 he founded his own weekly paper,* L'Express, *of which he is still editor.*

As a reserve officer, he volunteered for active service in July 1956, and served for six months in the French army in Algeria. He received various military honors, including the Croix de la Valeur Militaire.

A Note on the Type

This book is set in Electra, a Linotype face designed by W. A. Dwiggins (1880-1956), who was responsible for so much that is good in contemporary book design. Although much of his early work was in advertising and he was the author of the standard volume Layout in Advertising, Mr. Dwiggins later devoted his prolific talents to book typography and type design, and worked with great distinction in both fields. In addition to his designs for Electra, he created the Metro, Caledonia, and Eldorado series of type faces, as well as a number of experimental cuttings that have never been issued commercially.

Electra cannot be classified as either modern or old-style. It is not based on any historical model, nor does it echo a particular period or style. It avoids the extreme contrast between thick and thin elements which marks most modern faces, and attempts to give a feeling of fluidity, power, and speed.

This book was composed, printed, and bound by H. Wolff, New York. The paper was manufactured by P. H. Glatfelter Company, Spring Grove, Pennylvania. Designed by Harry Ford.

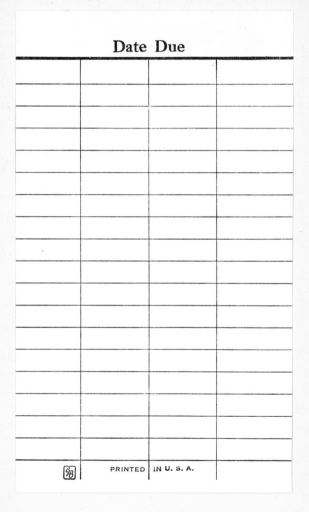

Date Due